Dedicated to the memory of

Laurence "Larry" Christopher Moriarty 1940 - 2019

&

Francis Christopher Gilbraith 1923 – 1995

James Gilbraith

Hooked On Hope

First published in Great Britain in 2019 by The Guild of Reason

A CIP Catalogue record for this book
is available from the British Library

ISBN 978-0-9930771-2-8

Cover design and typesetting by Ben Marsden
www.benmarsdendesign.co.uk

Edited by Matthew McKeown

Suggested Seasoning

Jackson C. Frank	*The Blues Run The Game*
Toots and the Maytals	*Funky Kingston*
Kurt Vile	*B'lieve I'm goin down*
She Keeps Bees	*Kinship*
Ugly Duckling	*Journey to Anywhere*
Aaron Neville	*Hercules*
The Flaming Lips	*Do You Realize?*
The Phantom Band	*Checkmate Savage*
Lyn Collins	*Think (About it)*
Moth Effect	*Crocodilians*
Modern Nature	*How To Live*
Alela Diane	*Cusp*
Joy Division	*Unknown Pleasures*
Scotch Bonnet Records Present	*Puffers Choice Vol 1 & 2*
Jackie Wilson	*Ain't no Pity in the Naked city*
Ian Brown	*Reign*
The Fall	*Telephone Thing*
Groundhogs	*Cherry Red*
Sugar Pi DeSanto	*Go Go Power*
James Brown	*Make it Funky (Live at the Apollo 1971)*
The Beta Band	*Dry the Rain*

Contents

1

Funky Kingston & the Eye of the Tiger

Funky Kingston, by Toots and the Maytals, is playing in my space capsule, and today's flight path involves briefly docking at the cracker factory for my final day of work. They asked for sixty willing candidates to take voluntary redundancy, and I was more than happy to oblige. There are, after all, only so many thoughts of *What the fuck am I doing with my life?* that a person can take, so after sixteen years of working in education, I have decided that I am cooked, done.

I think I've actually gotten shorter as a result of the despondency that this job has caused me; every day there feels like brain jail. I have a plan to open a shop and to buy and sell vintage goods and antiques. I need to be my own boss and walk my own walk, for good or bad. My motivation will come from having some skin in the game; it's sink or swim. I am totally exhausted from listening to others. For my own sanity, I need to grow a pair and give them all the primal scream of two fingers. My face can't mask my distance, apathy or disdain any longer. The spectre of my remaining natural life expectancy keeps reminding me that I can't waste another minute of precious time listening to bilge from designated bastards. Plus, I want to go fishing more often.

Yes, just one more suffocating eight-hour mission before I say goodbye to a few colleagues-cum-friends, and then I'll slingshot out of that unhealthy, negative atmosphere and re-enter the safety of the mothership – currently cloaked as a terraced house in Clitheroe, Lancashire – as a freewheeling, liberated man.

Toots is lighting up the cockpit like a cosmic supernova, displacing the January gloom with a bevy of warming imagery. Funky Kingston is where I think I'd like to be right now, as thoughts of smiling faces, cool rhythms, vibrant colours, roborant smells and hazy sunshine are evoked and enjoyed. A lovely, uplifting pace and an infectious sense of optimism glide through the track, through which Toots is asking us to believe in what he says and what he does. *Too late, Toots*, I think, *I'm way ahead of you*. If Funky Kingston was a person, I'm sure he would be a fisherman, and that he'd be bloody brilliant at it. He would be the infamous guy who everyone has heard of, but nobody has ever met.

Speaking of fishermen, the same local notaries have been returning to my ears like loyal homing pigeons over the last twenty years, through tales of heroic, potent consistency. These are people that I have never had the pleasure of meeting, and yet somehow, I seem to know the minute details of their lives, thanks to aural portals of folklore and idle gossip. There have been times where I have narrowly, and annoyingly, missed crossing paths with some of them by a day or even a matter of hours, and this only serves to amplify their legends. Each year, I embark upon an annual ghost hunt, walking the same ground as the true Ribble greats, to gain a first-hand snapshot of what makes them the elite.

In order to be elevated to 'Eye of the Tiger' status, one must catch between fifteen and thirty Ribble salmon per year, every year. To quantify these numbers within a tangible scale of achievement, you could compare it to a moonshot, and these angling astronauts are the cats that we measure the season against. I don't need a graph or a pie chart, or to trawl back through historical statistics, because there is no grey area here. I myself have caught a combined total of ten Ribble Atlantic salmon in the past two seasons, and in the last twenty-odd years, I've reached seasonal double figures only twice. Hundreds of salmon anglers chance their arm on the Ribble over the course of a season, with most being overjoyed to catch *one* fish, just to avoid blanking. Getting off the mark is the principal goal of the majority of ordinary salmon anglers, but then ordinary anglers are rarely spoken about by people stringing up in the carpark. To become a true river swami and get up into the thin air requires the average angler to hit the turbo-plus button.

You know the character, we all do, or at least we think that we do. The legend, the phantom of the riverbank; the solitary angler, who fishes in an expert shorthand and consistently catches. Their escapades are forever retold in their eternal absence, adding a romantic kudos that elevates them to the status of mystical river sage.

Secretly – ah yes, *very* secretly – we would all like to be revered and spoken about in the same exalted terms, and to have our odds-defying exploits recounted across numerous club carparks, describing how we battled a fresh, fighting fit and utterly wild wriggler while in the savage throes of a career-defining heart attack, or how we managed to catch over twenty salmon a season, every season. We would all prefer to travel in a gilt-edged cloud of quiet, smug confidence while deftly walking on rice paper, but before you get lost in another daydream filled with small glories, please bear in mind that being carried on the shoulders of your peers does not come easy or cheap. If you want to become a myth, you had better pay your dues both physically and mentally.

Now, let's explore the composition of this character, and then try and replicate the correct anatomy and uncover the golden components; to witness the fitness, so to speak. It's safe to imply that screaming around the inside bend is the attribute of obsessive behaviour. Our hero is undoubtedly an obsessive; history is littered with them. Flawed characters demented in their quest for perfection, and always demanding the same level of commitment from others. This quality is at the core of their being; it's the engine that eventually pushes the protagonist to the periphery of society where, cast away as an outsider, the obsessive can perform without fear.

Martin Hannet, the Factory Records producer who made the works of art that are the two Joy Division albums, Unknown Pleasures and Closer, had this obsession in spades. He went in knowing exactly what he didn't want; he didn't want average and he didn't want bland. Imagine bumping into a guy out on the Moors carrying a tape recorder and a microphone and asking him what he was up to, only to be informed that he was recording the silence. This same man once infamously ordered the band's drummer, Steven Morris, to take his drum kit up onto the roof and play 'faster but slower.' Hannet was brimming with wabi-sabi, as well as various other fatally twisted character flaws, and yet he was integral to the creation of something that was equal parts compelling and long-lasting. You see, it seems it did not matter what kind of state he was in; the key was that he turned up and did what was necessary. Hannet's isn't the only name on the cast list of obsessive creatives, either – far from it. The pages are perpetually added to, as square pegs continue to surprise and upset the round holes.

At this point in the piece, I should take the time to compare and contrast those flawed geniuses that rode the fiery curve of obsession and managed to get one element of their lives spectacularly right; the element for which they became famous or infamous. I'm not going to do that, though, because you're not stupid. You'll have your own examples, so you don't need mine.

Occasionally, a true story comes along that generates interest in the most incredible people. I myself was recently informed about an artist who died back in 2008, leaving behind more than fifteen thousand paintings, all of which were unceremoniously stuffed into his terraced house in Rossendale, Lancashire.

The artist, Dave Pearson, taught at Manchester Art College by day and then went home and painted all night. He did this for over thirty years, starting in his basement and then, once he'd filled that space, gradually moving from one room to the next until he had cornered himself on the top floor. The range and scale of some of the work is mesmerising. His output was beyond incredible; the house groaned under the sheer weight of myriad media forms. An extreme example though this may be, it's very much indicative of the compulsion to express oneself that carries the power to both fascinate and inspire.

Our Funky Kingston – this reggae song turned fisherman flesh – has his own groove on, as he stalks the waterways utilising extensive knowledge of the craft. His is a style cultivated by a lifetime of trial, error, watching, listening and countless hours spent bankside, a chief component of which is pathological optimism and persistence. While others are relaxing at home, looking out of the window and grimacing at foul weather, or finding themselves buried under a sickening workload of their own making, our hero is down at the river, regardless of conditions. Powered by the purest form of love, Funky Kingston hasn't the time for distractions or hobbies; his passions aren't blurred around the edges. There are no golf clubs in the boot, the squash racquet didn't get bought in the first place and he most certainly doesn't spend his weekends clad in Lycra as he rides out with the Ribble Wheelers, hoping that Giles will be there to discuss occupational up-skilling.

He has reconciled himself to experiencing his fair share of blank days, so you won't find him bleating online, responding to clickbait, crying into his Twitter feed or sharing what he had for breakfast with the denizens of Facebook. To him, the digital world represents an alien terrain forged from some warped witchcraft, to be viewed with the utmost contempt and suspicion. His natural habitat is the great outdoors, where he climbs trees, dances in the shadows, clambers on boulders, peers through the reeds and observes the riffles and the runs, happily committed to his lot in life.

At some point, the commitment test comes to us all, often without warning or consideration for convenience. In my case, it landed one afternoon around ten years ago, while I was accidentally fishing the River Lune. I say 'accidentally' because my original plan was to have a gentle autumn afternoon amble along the river, but upon spotting a few anglers scattered about and noting the level of the river (two foot on and running off, with the colour dropping out), I realised that there was a chance of catching a salmon. *Never bring a jelly to a cock fight*, I thought bitterly, after finding that the only tackle I had in the car was a six-foot spinning rod, an ABU spinning reel that was woefully undermanned with an eight-pound line and a small box of plugs that, luckily, contained a flying C. These were the remnants of a recent Sunday afternoon pike mooch on the Leeds and Liverpool canal, but, undeterred by a dearth of equipment or suitable clothing, I cast out a black and yellow twenty-six-gram Spintec flying C across the river at Deny Beck, just below the Crook o' Lune.

My sixth cast landed snugly at the far bank, and the always pleasantly surprising, no matter how familiar, heavy *bump-bump-bump* of a salmon bent the rod right over. I was in, and the strength of the fish, coupled with force of the river, put my little Jack outfit into an instant stress position. I managed to bring the fish across the river, only for it to get within fifteen metres of me and sulk in the current. I couldn't move the sod any further, and trying to force the issue with an eight-pound line would have been a dumb move. This unseen salmon was a good, fresh fish, lively as a buzz saw straining to take your thumb off, and it shot off on a twenty-metre run down the bank, past a large tree to my left. I'd steamed right in and I was loving this unexpected battle; the clichéd bent-double rod is arched under the lower branches that hung above the water.

Assessing my options, I soon deduced that I had just the two to choose from. The first was to jump in and continue the battle, flowing down the river past the tree, to a spot where I could bank the fish. However, looking down, I saw that the water was ink-black, and while I *thought* that it was only around four feet deep, it looked bloody bottomless. With the headline *'Idiot Drowns!'* flashing before my eyes, the only other choice appeared to be to hang on five minutes, not drown and see if the fish came back upstream, and then try to bully it without snapping.

I went with option two, and ten minutes later I was sat head in hands with a snapped line on the grass beside me. I didn't feel like walking anymore. I was left stupefied; my mind was pure static rage. What I actually felt like doing was, as Lamont so eloquently put it, going 'cracker-dog' and running amok with a chainsaw.

The following evening, I spoke to Lamont, my long-time fishing companion, who had just spent four hours in the exact same spot where I'd faltered. He relayed to me a conversation that had taken place between a couple of local rods fishing the opposite bank, who had shouted over that they'd seen 'some clown' hook and lose one yesterday. Ever the altruist, Lamont informed me that the consensus was that the bloke should have jumped in and gone around the tree, and that the local rod had ended his tale with a comment about the hapless angler having 'no commitment.'

I am not Funky Kingston. I'm Judy Garland.

The real Funky Kingston has the toughened psyche required to zero in on his pelagic prize; his ambition and talent are singular. Uninterested in aesthetics and above the indulgence of fretting over what tackle he uses, Funky Kingston isn't some wandering, lonely as a cloud, misty-eyed, nostalgic quasi-connoisseur, participating in a historical re-enactment. He doesn't think he's Isaac Crabtree (Lamont's brilliant description of anybody with a cane rod, in an amalgamation made from Isaac Walton and Mr Crabtree. 'Eh up, check out Isaac Crabtree!'), though I am totally confident that if either lived in our age, they would be driving transit vans full of gear. Isaac would be bivvied up with a slab of Stella and an eighth of weed, and using his bait boat to ferry contraband around a carp lake. Meanwhile, Crabbers would be examining his barometric watch, braiding up his bait-runner and checking for Tinder matches on his smartphone.

Funky Kingston's equipment is robust and purely functional; reliable performance being the source of its stoic beauty. These tools are replaced only when broken and, essentially, they are always ready to be deployed in the event of a guerrilla-style hit-and-run fishing opportunity suddenly arising. Despite never courting attention, his deeds somehow creep along the bootleg trail of the riverbank. His appearance is often confused with another's, and descriptions can be frustratingly vague. In my mind's eye, he looks like Dick Dastardly's forerunner, Jack Lemon's sneaky, underhanded character in *The Great Race*, the black-clad, moustachioed Professor Fate. Eyewitness accounts and sightings become ever more obscure. Lamont once tried to explain the appearance of an angler he was convinced I knew by saying, 'Yeah, yeah, you defo know him – speaks like this (he does an incomprehensible accent, which could be French Canadian, Welsh or perhaps Indian). He generally lurks around the bottom end, naan bread hairdo and sneaky Cornish eyes. Biggish fella, he sometimes wears a hat.'

Where does one even start the search engine memory bank roulette wheel of images based on that? What defines Cornish eyes, and what the fuck is a naan bread hairdo? I could hardly put out an all-points bulletin with that information.

'Zebra Three, Zebra Three, be on the lookout for a man with naan bread hair and Cornish eyes. He is wanted in connection with being annoyingly good at fishing – could be biggish and may or may not be wearing a fucking hat.'

Lamont was disappointed that I couldn't put a name to his encrypted description.

Too consistent to be an accidental Jedi, another essential element is that Funky Kingston boldly goes. He is happy to share a carpark that has been universally declared a derelict danger zone, reclaimed by Mother Earth and her most dogged doggers.* The murky reputation of a river beat that skirts a rough, John Carpenter-esque estate does nothing to dampen his spirits. He knows when it's safe to 'lurk around the bottom end.'

A true Funky Kingston, as seen through my eyes, is a great many things. His psychological makeup is, of course, subjective, seeing as though it currently sits in the corner of my own imagination. I don't own the copyright, but this I do know: the person you hear about in hushed, reverent tones is fuelled by the deepest love; the river is both their inspiration and aspiration, gifting them perfect clarity. With each fishing trip, they know that they are contributing to their own living artwork, constantly working on their own masterpiece, infinitely more elemental and beautiful than any dead thing hanging in a gallery or mounted on a plinth. Music genres pale in comparison to these panoramic adventures, where anglers wander in silent anticipation of what could happen next. The artist can be writer, director, producer, painter and poet all at once and at the same time, just as we, for an odd, eloquent and wonderful fleeting moment, can be faster but slower.

If that was as close as I'd ever get to becoming a myth, I would inhale a lungful of it every time, and with my newly acquired sole trader status, I owed it to myself to ride that wave all the way, until either it broke or I did.

***A quick note on dogging:** During a completely hypothetical discussion while grayling fishing the other day, we touched upon the subject of the twilight world of dogging. Lamont declared that it sounded 'overly complicated,' before adding, 'You have to make your car perform all sorts of coded signals to inform people what you would like to give or receive, and what form of recourse you require... even a small misunderstanding could have very unpleasant consequences.' As a result of this conversation, Lamont and I plan to spend the next close season conducting some unsavoury, gritty field research, ahead of publishing a guidebook, *Dogging Do's and Don'ts.*

2

Map Not to Scale

It's not enough that the fish are nearly always impossible to catch, if indeed they are even there, or that most decent clubs have an average waiting list of about three years, but when the blue-sky day arrives and you're finally welcomed into the club of choice, you must then navigate the new water that you have at your disposal. Sounds easy, doesn't it? A nice, casual walk along the river, reviewing your newly joined clubs' hand-drawn waters map, which looks like it's been professionally drawn by a pissed-up, haunted polygraph machine.

The carpark is clearly marked, easy. Pop your car in there, using the combination in the handbook to unlock the padlock, open the gate, drive in and shut the gate behind you; it's a doddle. OK, so now you tackle up and look at the map. The best thing to do is march to the top of the beat and work your way down, while carefully memorising the pool names on your map. Only now do you start to realise the enormity of your task; the map has more names than a Monopoly board, and it's a mixture of landmarks – some former, some current, some bizarre, some requiring a mental reach

– local slang and just downright wrongness. So, you walk off in search of Fiddler's Hole (heaven forbid that you have to ask where it is. 'I'm looking for Fiddler's Hole. I've heard that someone had one out of the back end.'), Sparks Pit and Dangerous Corner, with your mind boggling at the thought of how Fiddler's Hole got its ominous moniker. Your map tells you up front that it's not to scale, so at least you know that the beat is longer than four inches. I love that, you know. I love that the Committee *actually* discussed it.

'We'd better let the members know that the map isn't to scale.'

Perhaps they take a particularly dim view of their membership, but at least they stop short of writing *'Not suitable for human consumption'* on the handbook.

Starting at the bottom, you mentally tick off the Salmon Rocks (those sound full of promise), go past the innocuous-looking Run Hole and up to about eight blades of grass emerging from the river, no further than a rod's length out, marked Duck Island. Finding the Whirlpool isn't as easy as the name would suggest. You're picturing screaming sailors, shipwrecks, roaring winds and nature screaming its heart out, but the reality is a jolting anticlimax of the river gently running over shallow gravel and quietly creating a slow back eddy, which causes you to do a double take as you compare your map and the actual river.

Having reached the point where the river takes a left turn, you realise that you're at Dangerous Corner, and looking up you see the overhead power cables that give this bend its name. The power lines give off a nice Sonic Youth-style static fuzzed hum, and sport an exotic selection of spinners tangled around the black clad cables, providing the first hint of a tactical route that you may wish to follow. Judging by the number of flying condoms wrapped and snapped by terrified anglers not wanting to be incinerated in their wading boots, this looks like a good place to spin a black flying C. They aren't alone up there; the gang's all here, including an array of small bubble floats still attached to various sets of colourful sea trout flies.

You decide to walk around a pool named Suicide – *life ain't easy for a pool named Sui* – acknowledging that the more prudent move is to view this in low water, rather than take a cautious yet blind leap of faith into the unknown. After all, there must be a reason why it got its name, which presumably serves the practical purpose of warning the world-weary and confused salmon angler that this pool demands both attention and respect. Don't be getting in here half-cut from the night before or nursing an injury; it's probably better to follow somebody else down first and see what happens. This is a job for Hypothetical Peter (don't worry, I'll explain later). Maybe Peter hasn't read his map, so you tell him it's called Susan's Pool, as opposed to Suicide, which in the world of safe wading could be a PR disaster. You can ark an eyebrow as you watch Peter cast, step and then gently vanish into the black abyss, like a pole float on a roach-filled lily pond, while jotting a quick mental note, *Oh, that's why!* You can then play the hero and help poor, spluttering Hypothetical Peter back onto the safety of the bank, remarking on how inappropriate this pool's name is.

Next, you gaze over a six-foot overhang, down into the soulless Sparks Pit, black-looking and empty, as you gulp and glance up at more power lines buzzing in quiet menace above, and you wonder just why the hell you joined this club in the first place. It didn't look like this on the website, with all those smiling, vibrant faces and beautiful fish, complemented by photographs of stunning countryside on a gloriously sunny day, telling a starkly different tale. There certainly wasn't anybody laid out prone, smouldering and gnarled, while being stretchered onto an air ambulance. Looking directly at you is the looming blot on the landscape that is the local cement factory, with its ever-billowing chimney, eerily reminiscent of *Blade Runner.* It dawns on you that if you said these beat names aloud while staring into a mirror, something terrible would happen, while saying them backwards could possibly open a portal to somewhere even less nice than where you are right now. Maybe a deceased former club chairman spat out these names via a Ouija board decades ago, at some clandestine backroom committee séance.

'Arnold Fiddler, are you there? Speak to us, Arnold. We can't decide on the beat names.'

On most salmon rivers, the pools arrive at their names through obvious means, mainly because of the foreign objects that have been deposited there:

- Fridge Pool – there's a fridge in it.

- Bathtub Pool – concrete poured into a bath, left to set and then removed from its bath mould, before being dropped into a featureless spot in the river to create a salmon lie.
- Safe Pool – similar situation to Bathtub Pool. Visualise the scene: roadside pool, van pulls up, two-to-four men jump out and slowly manhandle a medium-sized safe, which they then drop into the river before disappearing double-quick sharp.
- Vauxhall Astra Pool – you couldn't make it up. I do hope that they deliberately jumped it into the river with the sole intention of making a half-decent holding pool, rather than it being a case of some gormless goons, ripped to the tits on Buckfast and barbiturates, thinking that they were living some video game. I like the idea of salmon anglers hatching a scheme to improve habitat, and I could imagine their train of thought: *These salmon are running straight through here – if only we could make them slow down. What's big and heavy and on wheels? 'Stevie, what're you doing with that old Astra?'* There's a sort of elegant, romantic Butch and Sundance rapport in between the lines.*

Directions to the prime spots can be head-scratchingly fuzzy, e.g. *Turn right where the oak tree used to be.* This kind of 'help' isn't even mischievous; you're really supposed to know where the tree was. I've been ushered down to the Boiler House before, only to wonder if I'm in the right bastard spot, as there isn't a single visible sign of any form of heavy industry.

Later, in the carpark, the helpful club angler informs me that I was indeed in the right place. I ask him why it was named the Boiler House, and his response is that there *had* been a boiler house there, which *had* belonged to the mill. I look around and see no mill, only a housing estate, and without the slightest hint of irony, he looks at me blankly and verbally pokes me in my third eye, by enlightening me with the news that both the mill and its boiler house were demolished in 1962.

Namaste, you bastard.

From the Gas Pipe to Fiddler's Hole, it can be a real minefield for the uninitiated, but it can also seem very exciting to the new club member who's keen as mustard to immerse themselves in this bright new world. You can spend hours looking for just the right colour of plastic carrier bag that's stuck in a tree on the opposite bank, after some wizened old 'crinkle cut' (Lamont's euphemism for anybody over the age of sixty-five) angler has pointed you in the direction of his secret honey hole (in two hundred attempts, he's nabbed two salmon), only to find out that the names you've learned are totally different to those known to the locals. Oh yes, we locals often have many names for exactly the same spot: Sewage Works, Talbots and Morts are all the same beat on the Ribble. Never mind the language barrier, although the older I get, the more economical I am with words.

I'm reminded of the time I was asked what type of egg I was eating.

'En egg,' I answered.

'I know it's an egg,' my friend Charlotte replied, 'but what type?'

Confused, I merely repeated, 'En egg,' before adding, 'An egg from a 'en.'

Yes, the letter H has been dropped like it never happened, leaving Charlotte, an English teacher, in peals of laughter and with tears in her eyes.

'Oh, a *hen* egg!' she cried, while I, stern-faced, continued to say 'En egg,' over and over, as though it was her fault that she couldn't understand my yipped English.

Most anglers I meet tend to get by using a combination of facial expressions and body language, but the real analogue masters of the understated can communicate via breathing and subtle eyebrow twitches. A slow, deliberate exhale, or a sudden intake of breath coupled with a narrowing of annoyed eyebrows, is sometimes the extent of their entire river report.

The majority of beat names have a reasonable, logical explanation behind them, but there are some that are so out of left field that they can make your mind hurt and require a deep-sea dive into imagination. I'll give you an example:

Baby Elephant is a spot on the Ribble, near Clitheroe, and Lamont and I have both tried to find out how it got its name. We thought that there must be something like a grey rock that looks slightly like an infant pachyderm's back. It'd make sense – I've heard worse rationales – but guess again, and first clear your head of any internal clutter. After much research and conversations with various anglers, we were told the following: (take a deep breath and get your mind right. Ready? OK)

It's called Baby Elephant because there's a deepish hole midstream, which a baby elephant could stand in, fully immersed, without you seeing it.

Gestate on that!

You want a banana shot to bend your head? Well, we've got you covered with beats named for what could potentially be concealed under the water. Here's your map, now crack the fuck on, and remember not to forget that, like the salmon angler's hopes, this map is not to scale.

*Never ever leap cars off bridges into rivers, even if it would create a killer salmon lie.

3

Terry Cracking

Most of us salmon anglers balance watchfully on the frontier of delusion, but obviously there are some exceptions. Lamont and I are stealthily hacking our way through the twisted, mangled, obstacle-strewn river, hugging wood on the way to one of our favourite spots. These days, this pet spot isn't as productive as it once was, and we are subsequently trading on past glories, but it remains rooted in our hearts due to two things.

First, our own magic moments of unexpected success fishing it, and second, the fact that there's never anybody else here.

We are both eager beavers this fine March morning. The weather is on Prozac, and nature's mellow spring vibrations are as infectious as a weeping crimson cold sore. The big water has run off, and we are looking at a very manageable, perfect ten remaining inches before we are back down to a summer level. We have one net between us, our pockets are filled with essentials and our fly rods are already rigged. We're rocksteady ready, no bullshit (be mindful of the BS, as it stalks you from every angle).

Lamont is in a chipper mood, having blown off work in favour of three hours with me and the river, and as we march on, I am almost at bliss point (in the formulation of food products, the 'bliss point' is the amount of an ingredient, such as salt or sugar, needed optimise deliciousness without it becoming oversaturated) because at this moment in time and space, on planet earth, I'm doing exactly what I want to do. Suffice to say, the only way is down from here.

I am forever waiting to hear what Lamont has to say with bated breath. His company is a dizzying rollercoaster of uncertainty. At any given moment, he could utter something so sublime or outrageous that it leaves you appalled, floored or weeping with uncontrollable laughter. Today, he has already compared an acquaintance's complexion to that of a suet steak pudding.

He looks around the wood in this sumptuous, narrow moment of spring, and says to me, 'Terry is looking out for us all today.'

'Who's Terry?' I ask, as I negotiate a tricky fence using a very wobbly, dilapidated wooden stile, which frankly looks more dangerous than the guillotine, being nicely topped-off with a lovely long piece of wader-killing barbed wire (these woods are littered with the haunting, sombre cries of mangled anglers bemoaning their newly punctured waders).

'Terry Cracking,' he says, 'the guardian of the woods, tree protector and river trustee.'

I search my limited memory storage for the file on

Terry Cracking, hoping to put a face to the name of this champion of nature. 'Do I know him? Have we met?'

'I doubt it,' he says, hauling a stiff-jointed trailing leg over the stile and joining me in Chinese airspace, as we enter the final section of our walk. 'Nobody has.'

He looks at me quizzically.

I stop walking and turn to face him square on. I'm now off -the-scale confused, and I decide to question him further. 'What do you mean, "Nobody has?" If this bloke has done all this amazing work, *somebody* must have met him. He must have encountered *someone* along the way! *Terrence Cracking* – sounds like a stage name for a Reggae performer.' I find myself agitated and exasperated, arms spread wide apart as I channel an imaginary MC introducing Mr Cracking. 'And now here he is, the guardian of the woods, the tree protector, the mighty river trustee...'

Lamont simply smiles and shakes his head, like I'm some poor, deluded fool. 'No, no, *no!* He's not a man, he's a spirit. The spirit of the woods – the angler's friend. Everyone knows Terry Cracking.'

It's now my turn to shake my head and smile, as I knowingly give in to the septic shards of his unwell mind. It's hard, but I try to retain some composure. 'Well, I'm fifty, and I've never heard that particular piece of folklore before. In fact, I've never heard those two words spoken together before.'

Lamont looks genuinely shocked, almost concerned, by my comments. I'm all-in now, so I opt to concede.

'Fine, tell me everything you know about Terry Cracking,' I say, 'but I bet that you're the only living person on the planet who's ever heard of him.'

He then spends half an hour recounting what his father had told him all about Mr Cracking when he was but a boy, including how, in actual fact, our Terry had been going out with Mother Nature until she had finished with him for getting up too early. Apparently, this had got right on her wick. Throughout the telling of this vivid tale, there is zero sense of irony, either visually or tonally, from the narrator. He ploughs on with the relationship dynamics, explaining that Terry 'couldn't be doing with her.'

We reach our tranquil destination and sit down on our 'ring in sick' bench, looking down the beat. I smile again at Lamont's perfectly delivered turn of phrase, 'couldn't be doing with her,' imagining how Charlotte would go about explaining the etymology of that one to a Language class. So eloquent and to the point, yet simultaneously vague and understated.

I ask Lamont to elaborate on what it was about Mother Nature's behaviour that Terry couldn't be doing with, but he is now slowly stepping into the river and starting to pull line from his reel, in order to put a cast out across the flow. I resolve to save the rest of this conversation for the walk back to the carpark, and hop over another fence and scoot two hundred yards above him, to where there are a couple of runs that are always (rarely) worth a chuck. Behind me is open sage green farmland, to my left is the bastard wood that

I've just exited and across from me is more unbroken farmland stretching up towards the town of Longridge. Everything feels *right,* but that doesn't stand for much when an angler's default setting is blind optimism.

Lamont is edging slowly down the pool below me; the pool that I want to be in. The run I'm in looked better than it actually is, unless I'm approaching it with the wrong tactics. Over the years, I have tried various leaders, tips and fly setups, but I've only ever briefly hooked one fish. The water funnels very heavily immediately past large boulders in the central part of the river, which forces the water past the bank that I'm standing on. In my opinion, the fish must come through hugging our bank, but who knows? Even if I'm correct in my thinking, the odds of being there at the exact moment when a fish passes through are brain-twistingly, ridiculously, massively long.

Stupid bloody salmon.

Lamont is in the groove and is fluently casting into the head of the main pool; his tall, willowy frame reminding me of an Alberto Giacometti sculpture. He is using a full floater with a ten-foot slow sink tip – the depth of the river here goes from one to four feet, so we aim to get our flies down to about two feet – and he'll be fishing one of a Verminator, a stoat's tail or a Black Shrimp. I'd be very surprised if he's thinking outside the fly box and trying something new. After all, we're on the Ribble, where it's extremely difficult to gauge if something innovative is going to be a success. You could quite easily be fishing for a year and not get a pull, so we stick to trusted patterns. Progress is awfully demanding on time, and besides, we prefer analogue. We're definitely of the 'stick it on their nose' school.

Just as I begin pondering what Terry Cracking would look like, I see Lamont's rod bend and start dipping under the force of a fish. Automatically, I assume that it's a trout, but he looks quickly over his shoulder and shouts that it's a decent fish. I get out of the water straightaway and walk down the bank, to watch and get the net ready. Lamont is nearly a quarter of the way across the river, and the fish makes a steady run downstream. He looks both excited and anxious as the fish changes direction, pulling across the current and racing towards the far bank. However, he keeps the pressure on and coaxes it back to mid-current, all the while taking slow steps to the left. For a few brief moments, it's a stalemate, but then the fish goes on a bullish charge downstream and Lamont gives it some line and lets it run.

The fish's run slows and Lamont winds in, getting over his prey and taking charge. We are at the halfway point, and there are two more runs into the mid-current before he gives me the signal to get in with the net. I position myself downstream, and as the fish goes onto its side, I quickly slide the net under it. *Bingo!*

Lamont looks elated as he stares skyward and bellows, 'I LOVE YOU, TERRY!' and we take a moment to admire the beautiful sight of his first fish in eighteen months (he blanked in 2018).

The barbless double Black Shrimp comes out easily

with the forceps. It's a lovely fresh spring fish of about sixteen pounds, and Lamont gently holds it in the current for about five minutes until it gives on last strong kick and is gone.

You couldn't fake the expression on his daft, smug face. The total surprise when you finally get one is an injection of pure joy. So many moving parts need to come together for it to happen, and when it does, it's somewhat surreal. Lamont walks up the steep bank and takes an imperious seat on our bench, which has now become his temporary throne. He looks down and gestures for me to get in, as he takes out of his breast pocket a slim, dented hip flask and a compressed, contorted, cellophane-wrapped sandwich. I can't help but look up at him and smile as he enjoys his winning post moment; he's earned it by grafting harder than gravity. I tell him that I thought there was one in this pool, and then turn and start back towards it, conscious of the fact that I'm now going to have to be a captive audience to a turbo-bushy Lamont. I haven't got time to rest, though. If there's one in the pool, that means there's every chance of there being another.

'Victory has one hundred fathers, while defeat, my dear friend, is an orphan,' comes his opening salvo.

He is well and truly in the saddle, and I'm the doe-eyed steer that he's playfully trying to lasso and hogtie. I ignore him, but internally I have become the falling man pictured in the poster for the Alfred Hitchcock movie, *Vertigo*.

'I can't wait to tell Bunny when I get in,' he

continues, referring to Bunny Wailer (Sir), his dog, who he claims is a tripe hound, an original and traditional Lancashire breed, bred for... fuck only knows. It looks like its two dogs welded together, ginger, broken-coated and just about a foot-and-a-half tall and two-feet long. At the business end, it has a Tigerfish smile and an elongated crocodile terrier face, mounted in front of a bushy lion's mane that peters out mid-body at a smooth back end, hence the cut and shunt looks.

Informing Bunny Wailer is as close to a social media announcement as Lamont will get, other than perhaps a hastily deleted, booze-induced swift digital bullet aimed at our private *Salmon! Salmon! Salmon!* WhatsApp group. Thus, unless Bunny is on Twitter or Instagram, it's destined to remain our little secret.

'Me and Bunny were out early doors this morning, and I heard a bunch of starlings twittering, telling me that today was gonna be the day,' he informs me. 'They all knew that it was *right*. Even the flowers had a spring in their step.'

Bear in mind, this is a man who once referred to Neil Armstrong as 'that moon dude.'

I cast and step, wishing that I had my iPod and headphones in for protection while watching the fly line steadily arc around from right to left.

'This is all the magical work of Terry Cracking,' he's still going on. 'My dad was right. Terry does favour anglers.'

I have no choice but to engage him, even though I know that he will prey on my thoughts and remarks.

'So, why did Mother Nature chuck him, then? You never finished explaining.'

'Why indeed? It turns out that good old Mother Nature found out about the golden rule – you never date the staff,' he shakes his head wistfully.

It's never before occurred to me to deploy a can of CS gas, but today, I think that one lobbed gently under Lamont's throne may be merited. It would be quite pleasant to watch him vanish in a cloud of toxic smoke.

Exiting the pool, I'm desperate to give it twenty minutes' rest before going through it again, but time has stomped all over me once more. I traipse back through the newly named Terry's Wood, while Lamont levitates his way back to the car, high on the supreme wisdom of all known and unknown knowledge. I trail him down the single-track path that weaves through Terry's hometown and back into the farmyard, where our club's carpark is situated. It's approaching lunchtime, and we are enjoying this beautiful, fish-catching spring day as we meet another angler along the way. Neither of us recognises this fellow, but we clock that he's dressed for chasing salmon. I wait to take Lamont's lead, wondering if he'll crow about his success or play it cool and sit tight, or even attempt a misdirect.

'ow do, 'owt doin'?' the stranger greets us. 'You came out wood. I didn't know there was a fly run in wood. I usually fish the run downstream.'

Lamont immediately reverts to pidgin English in an effort to appear casually friendly, but ends up sounding like he's doing an awful impersonation of Bob

Hope's Native American act. 'We come out of wood, but do no good,' he says. 'Wood bad, downstream better.'

What the fuck? I think, staring at him in bemusement.

'Oh, right then,' the stranger says, looking at the wood and then downstream, obviously confused. 'Cheers, lads.'

'Tight lines,' we wish him in unison, as we wave goodbye.

In the privacy of the carpark, I can't help but start mimicking Lamont's schtick as we tackle down. 'Hey Big Chief, what's with the Son of Paleface medicine man routine? Why you no tell of fish?'

'Terry warn of stranger danger,' Lamont said thoughtfully. 'Big Chief listen to Terry and not mug himself.'

After much laughter, I shake his hand and formally congratulate him as we share a single slug from his hip flask, and then formulate an action plan for stealing some more time before he goes off with his prize. I jump into my car and catch up on some work while listening to Aaron Neville sing Hercules, satisfied that this superb mellow, soulful groove is just the ticket for my ride across the restful landscape.

Like the bird on the wing,
I just want to be free enough to do my thing...

Amen to that.

Later, at home, my wife Anne Marie nonchalantly asks if I had a good time with Lamont on the river, and I reply by asking her if she's ever heard of a woodland sprite named Terry Cracking.

'Light the fire, and let me at least open a bottle of wine before you tell me,' she rolls her eyes and smiles.

Love is all around. I'm in a good place now, and it's still only March. I must be Hercules.

4

Championship Versions

As I'm sure that you're only too aware by now, I don't really like cheating on the Ribble. It's my own form of sadism to hardly see or catch any fish, even though I try harder and harder each season. It's like an Anaconda; the more you struggle, the tighter it squeezes. Fortunately, for me the opportunity to cheat never swims into my vicinity too often, but when it does, the outcome generally boils down to the twin bottom lines of time and money. Both are always tight.

The ritual of a Friday teatime pint runs deep in me. Muscle memory and learnt behaviour leaves me feeling fidgety and odd if I'm not in a pub by six on the final working day of the week. On this particular Friday, I have arranged to meet Lamont for a swift pint. He said that he wants to ask me something.

I enter the bar and head directly to our not-so-secret snug in the secluded back room of the Mill, in Clitheroe. This former textile mill, originally built in the 1820s, is now home to a thriving complex of various businesses, including a brewery and a cinema, and it also boasts Britain's largest bar. The makeover has been completed with the utmost sympathy for the building's heritage, with machinery being left behind as statement pieces, and the original thick mill flagstones, metalwork and beams remaining exposed in a quietly shabby chic nod to the past. The fixtures and fittings were repurposed and upcycled using ingenuity and a keen eye for design, and the result is a fantastic-looking bar fitted with great seating, which always features plenty of guest ales. Behind the main bar, there are several smaller rooms, and it is into one of these – the one with a log burner and two fantastic large leather wingback club chairs – that I turn while nursing a pint of Bowland Brewery's gentle Boxer Blonde. I can see Lamont's angular frame poking out from behind one of the large wingbacks by the fire.

Looking serious, he gestures for me to take a seat and asks if I've come alone. Only he could make such a mundane, everyday situation escalate abruptly to the point where the tension is palpable. He sits up straight and rearranges himself in the grand old seat, and then takes a sip of his rich, obscure dark porter and begins.

'The old boy was meant to be on a ketogenic diet,' he says sullenly. 'Zero alcohol or grains, and absolutely no carbs. His wife was twenty years younger than him and lived on a treadmill, like a hamster. You know the type, utterly fucking joyless – weighing food and pretending to be happier for it. He was on his fifth week when he cracked. He set up a small table in his garage and was tucking into a dreamy twenty-two-inch chilli and salami pizza, freshly cooked and delivered under the cover of darkness. She was supposed to be at the gym doing a spin class, but it turns out that she wasn't, and while he was hurriedly eating his contraband, she was turning into the driveway and caught him bread-handed. The garage became a crime scene, as she deliberately ploughed straight into him, pinning him unconscious to the back wall of the garage. He was lucky not be killed, but he was badly injured – broken pelvis, hip and wrist. The impact deployed the airbag, leaving her unable to escape the vehicle while she screamed about a breach of trust. The neighbours called the police, and she's just got ten years for attempted manslaughter.'

My head spins as he continues.

'Anyhow, the guy who was hit with the motor was meant to be coming up to the Spey for a week in April. He usually has a full rod, so I thought that you and the Heron could come in for half a rod each. The old guy isn't up to it, I'm afraid. The whole sorry saga has really hit him for six. It's put him off pizza and left him walking like a crab.'

Lamont likes the odd week away, quietly enjoying four days on the Tweed every June, and even wangling a week's full rod with a party of fishers on the river Spey back in 2016. I don't know any of this group, but I was surprised when he told me that he had been asked if he would like to retain the rod. He must have been on his very best behaviour.

I need to drill down deep into this offer and find out what the true cost is. Lamont assures me that the whole week would swing in for £600, including diesel, cottage rental, food and fishing. I'd have to share a rod with the Heron, and would probably need a grappling hook to winch him out the river whenever it was my turn, but I could live with that. The only answer I could give was an emphatic 'Yes!' Yes to Spey, yes to Salmon and yes to pissing about and laughing for a week.

'Do you fancy splitting a pizza?' Lamont asks. 'I'm starving.' He then smiles and adds a footnote. 'Every cloud, eh?'

The invitation catches me completely flat-footed. *The Spey in April*, I think, *wow*. I automatically start to feel uncomfortable about the prospect of being away with Lamont for a whole week. Spending the occasional five hours on the river is one thing, but being fully immersed with him for a prolonged period would be something else altogether. You see, he never stops; his opinions and theories are always on the boil. I could be waist-deep in water and struggling with an upstream wind, and there's every chance that he'd be asking stuff like, 'Would you get your head frozen if you were diagnosed with a terminal illness, until a cure was found?' A week would be quite testing, but on the other hand, I could re-up on material. Embrace the yin and yang, while praying that the ghillie would rotate us on the beat, allowing everyone some vital *me* time.

I just need to get confirmation from my wife that she can manage while I'm away. She works full-time, and our children are aged seven and ten respectfully. A week away is a big ask.

As always, Anne Marie agrees instantly and

enthusiastically. Man, I love that woman; the sun never fails to shine with her. I came in from my meeting with Lamont giddy with drink and babbling about the Spey and a breach of trust, and Ams (Anne Marie) just smiled and said, 'I think you need to go, love. You'll have a great time, and we'll all be fine here.'

It was all I needed to hear. Time to do an equipment check.

Equipment Status Report

Vision Wading boots = *fucked*
Vision Waders = *multiple leaks – groin and inside knee rub, i.e. fucked*
Fifteen-season-old SST Patagonia wading jacket like a teabag = *fucked (without doubt the best piece of fishing clothing I've ever owned. It was perfect)*
Ten-year-old fifteen-foot Hardy Demon fly rod – couple of chips in the top section = *two thumbs up*
Greys multi-spool fly reel with wobbly spigot = *two thumbs up*
Four-seasons-old Snowbee 10/11 weight full floater = *properly fucked*

I'm skint, but there's hope yet. Sportfish do a deal where you can drip payments on an interest-free basis, so after skipping down the virtual aisles, clicking the mouse like it was my heels and going mental while loading my online shopping cart with shiny new rods, lines, switch outfits, spinning reels and God knows what else, I rein myself in, slap myself out of it and buy only the essentials.

I take the executive decision to spend £700 on Simms boots, waders and a jacket. I circle the square by telling myself that I'll get ten years out of the jacket, and if I get three years out of the boots and waders (no fucking way), it's a win. Having ended up piss-wet through on every visit to the river for the last eight months, I feel as though I deserve to get some new gear. However, I'm also worried that I'll appear to be some posh ponce casting his first line. I need to let people know that I'm only in this new clobber because of some financial mistake. I intended to tell the ghillie that these aren't my clothes yet.

Lamont and the Heron went up to Aberlour on the Saturday, and had enjoyed an evening in the Mash Tun, the same pub where I was to meet them. I'm on course to land at 7pm, after setting off from Clitheroe at 11am and gunning it there in one hit. I'm in an excited form of trance, absently driving a car filled with a mixture of football commentary and favourite feel-good albums. I am buzzing and, let's face it, I don't have anything to moan about – Lyn Collins's LP, Think (about it), won't allow it. My sole trader status has propelled me to soul trader, meaning no more bullshit cap in hand booking of holidays and being grateful to some bell-end manager for the privilege. I am poorer but richer since leaving my old job in the cracker factory. You can't buy time, baby. Remember that.

Lamont flies me in the last few directions as I pull around the corner to the Mash Tun, and it truly is love at first sight. Lamont and the Heron are there waiting, each sporting ear-to-ear grins and open arms. Man, I am happy. After team hugs and handshakes, they walk me to the river Spey, and it's love at first sight once again. We stand on the footbridge and look up towards the Boat Pool, eyes wide and breath held until the silence is broken by Lamont asking, 'Well?'

The word hangs in the air as a beautiful silver salmon leaps clear of the water, approximately one hundred and fifty yards upstream. *An actual salmon running*, I'm almost incredulous. On the Ribble, I can count the number of running fish I see annually on one hand, no shit. Before I get the chance to tell Lamont how I feel, another two fish show. I should have prepared a statement before I left the house, just in case; something profound and pithy. All I can manage is a dazed, 'It's fucking wonderful.' I just needed the Beta Band to briefly reform and play a guerrilla gig in the Mash Tun now, and I would spontaneously combust.

We adjourn to the pub for a couple of drinks, and I really enjoy the warm, vibrant ambience. It quickly becomes apparent that Lamont had told anyone with a pulse the story of his spring salmon from the Ribble, although there is no mention of the helpful woodland sprite, Mr Terence Cracking. I am not here to piss on his parade, though. I'm in with Lamont for the long haul. My mission is to quietly observe his chameleon-like social skills.

Whisky Galore springs to mind as I take in the charted, rich Speyside heritage of all the world-famous local distilleries that are pictured on the walls, and gaze behind the bar at a whisky menu that is thicker than a phonebook. *Do they still have phonebooks?* I wonder. It is about two-and-a-half inches thick, and I doubt that anybody could drink their way through it without succumbing to liver failure. The Mash Tun seems to be a place for conversation and contemplation. *Bonus.*

Optimism is at full gas now; we have hit the launch button and are strapped in for the ride. *What a place this* is, I think, still having one more surprise to come in the form of our digs, which are up the road in nearby Archestown.

I presume that the accommodation will be rough and ready at best, which I've no problem with. In fact, I'd happily sleep in the car. What greets us, however, is a fantastic four-bedroom open plan cottage with all the mod cons. Again, Lamont looks immensely pleased with himself. I get the wine out of the car.

Upon entering the cottage, I quickly realise that we are not alone. Sat in the kitchen are two men in their early sixties who I don't know. Lamont shakes hands with them as they say in unison, 'The Captain's here.'

My eyes narrow as I home in on a gleeful-looking Lamont, and I am hurriedly introduced to George and Andy. I soon find out that they are both veterans of the Spey, who have been coming up here annually for forty years or more.

What perplexes me is the use of the term 'Captain' in reference to Lamont.

Sleeping Arrangements
Downstairs bedroom one: Heron and Me
Downstairs bedroom two: Andy and George
Massive upstairs en-suite, incl. large double bed: 'The Captain'

What shit has he pulled here? I can't stop asking myself. *The* fucking Captain?

I don't know much, but this I am certain about: Lamont is a sociopathic psychopath. He ticks all the boxes, even some that they haven't thought about.

Over a glass of wine, Andy and George tell me that Lamont is to be called the Captain for the week because he is in charge, and I wonder what kind of Ted Bundy-style charm offensive he must have been on with this lot. He likes being the Captain; his body language gives him away, shoulders pulled back and chest puffed out.

The fucking Captain! It's like giving Lance Armstrong the keys to the pharmacy and expecting him not to have a dabble.

The Captain outlines his rota for the cottage. George will cook breakfast every morning, aided by Andy, while the Heron and I wash up and keep the place tidy. I am also publicly given the job of fetching the Captain his daily newspaper. For his part, the Captain is in charge of the TV remote, so elevated is his status.

No wonder he loves these away days, I think. *He reinvents himself.*

I am reminded of the Lamont I know recently phoning me, following another road rage incident.

A driver of a VW Golf had cut him up, almost forcing him off the road in his van. Please bear in mind that this is Lamont's own edited version of events.

'I pulled over and asked him to get out of his car,' he began.

I doubt that. It's far more likely that he would have leapt out, jumping up and down while demanding that the other driver get out of the fucking car.

'The driver of the Golf started doing the wanker sign at me,' he continued, 'so I lost my temper and tried to open his door. I was very verbal at this point, and quite agitated. The driver of the Golf then started laughing at me, pointing at a dashboard camera that was filming everything. I backed away, now laughing myself, and got back inside the van and shot off. It's going to go viral, isn't it?'

My guess is that it was Lamont who had cut the Golf driver up, and the bit where he says he was verbal and quite agitated means that, in actual fact, he was going dog shit mental. That's my Lamont; the one who wants his head frozen and once bought a nylon track suit, so that he could poach a day ticket on the Ribble; the one who wanted to go on the TV show *Dragons' Den* with his invention, the Angler's Friend, which was a pair of small false hands that an angler could wear while holding a fish, in order to make the catch look bigger on photographs. 'That's how it's going now, on the internet and that,' he'd explained, and now *he's* in charge. These things really do have a way of creeping up on us. Certain circumstances cannot be explained.

I'm half-expecting him to dress for dinner and then descend from his sumptuous bedroom wearing a cravat, like Noel Coward.

Over our evening meal back down at the Mash Tun, I receive the low-down. The beat is split into a top and a bottom. Andy and George will be half a rod each, with Lamont enjoying a full rod. FYI, a full rod means that you can fish all day, while a half rod indicates sharing. In mine and the Heron's case, we will be alternating hourly.

The beat is Kinermony, which is marshalled by a ghillie named Davey. By all accounts, Davey is a fantastic guy, who knows the beat inside out, upside down, back to front and the full three-sixty. Protocol dictates that we will meet at the top beat hut at 9am in the morning to meet Davey, and then he'll tell us who is going where.

I am both tired and full of anticipation as I hit the sack. I am also surprised to see that the Heron doesn't sleep in his jacket and waders, having been previously convinced that he never takes them off. Whenever I am feverishly trying to set up on our local patch at some ridiculously early pre-work splash and dash mission, if his car isn't already there, I know it won't be long until I hear it coming around the corner. The faint rumble of his engine drawing closer can cause me to panic and flap, to the point that I once hastily tied my fly onto my leader without first running my line through the eyes of the rod. As the Heron pulled into the carpark to see me visibly fumbling to try and get to and through our top pool first, I watched on aghast as he got out of the car already in his jacket and waders, with rod set up and collapsed into four pieces. 'Morning,' he said dryly, not even breaking stride as he made his way up the riverbank, 'think I'll have a quick look at the top.'

Meanwhile, I was stood faffing like Mr Bean, wishing that I had a poisoned blow dart to drop him like a stone with.

Day One

Stunning breakfast cooked and served by George, and while he and Andy enthusiastically reminisce about their forty years on the Spey, I go and get the Captain his paper. The Heron puts eight bottles of Bowland Brewery's Hen Harrier in the boot, and I can't tell you how excited I am. There were a lot of moving parts that got me here, leaving me with a sense of guilt – a nagging feeling that I shouldn't be having so much fun. It's very weird. Don't worry, though, it passes!

We drive to the top beat and meet up with Davey. The beat is glorious, with manicured banks and pine trees. It's almost lit up, you know, just *brighter* somehow. Lots of features from top down: quicker water, narrow channels flowing to a wider steady pool that looks good enough to eat. The hut has a seat running the length of it, overlooking the river. White-painted walls, green tin roof and green-painted window frames. We all take a seat around the table within the hut, and Davey greets us with a warm smile. He is an imposing figure with handsome features, tall and heavyset; he looks to be in his mid-forties. His two Labradors have already brought us some pinecones to throw, but he warns against this if we ever want to get any fishing done. Davey puts a brew on and goes through the catch reports, letting us know our prospects. The water level is not perfect, but not far off. Davey sits at the head of the table with his hands in his pockets, as he tells us where we will each be fishing in the morning session. Lamont, the Heron and I will be on the lower beat, known as the Boat Pool. That's where we saw the fish show last night.

Upon arriving at the Boat Pool, we are all grinning like schoolboys. The hut there is a smaller, more basic shed, with a kettle, table and a couple of plastic patio chairs and a bench outside. This pool looks astonishing, as a fast run empties into the head of the pool, giving it a decent pull for over fifty metres. Two rods can only be in the water at any one time, and the Captain and the Heron are going in first. The Heron takes up position halfway up the neck of the quick water, while Lamont is set to get in below him, only to turn and call for me to get in while he makes a brew. I decline, waving him away in the direction of the river, but he insists.

I am fishing my full floater with a ten-foot fast sink tip, seven-foot Maxima fifteen pounds leader to a Rapala knot and a size-twelve double cascade. I get in the River Spey right outside our hut, with the Heron further up to my left. I take line off my reel and false cast to get my line out in front of me. I double Spey cast and my line lands nice and square in front of me. Behind me, Lamont has filled the kettle and is stretched out swinging on the doorway, watching me.

I repeat the cast and watch my line come around. I feel a fish hit my fly and I wait before lifting the rod, and quickly realise that it's a salmon. Talk about unprepared! I could not believe it. The fish rips off into a downstream run, and Lamont is getting animated on the bank above my right shoulder. The Heron is reeling in and making his way out of the river. The fish is now taking me to the far bank – I am totally shitting it. Fully aware at how bizarre this situation is, I am also aware that unless I land this fish, I will have missed an astonishing opportunity. The fish now turns its attention towards going upstream, and I am feeling every amplified bump and pull. My mind is racing, awash with self-doubt, dread and fear. Lamont is telling me to keep my rod up, as I tighten my drag on the reel. The fish goes again, and I use my hand as the drag to keep the tension on. I get the fish into mid-current and it launches airborne, but I hold the fuck on. I notice that the smiling Heron is filming me on his phone.

'Stop filming me, I'll lose it,' I yell. 'Get the net!'

I'm trying to sound calm, but in truth I am petrified. I would rather crash through a fully-paned greenhouse than lose this fish. I hear them both discussing where the net is, and it begins to feel like a conspiracy. Lamont gets in next to me; the fish is now under control, and I get it on its side and glide it towards the edge of the river. Lamont tries to gently grab the wrist of its tail, but he misses and succeeds only in making it steam off again on an agitated run. Again, we go through the motions, but this time the wrist is cradled and we have the fish. Sparkling silver, eleven pounds of total, complete, unadulterated, pure raggy bastard.

Second fucking cast, imagine that! It wasn't even my turn, either. I hadn't so much as contemplated such a thing happening. The fish is quickly unhooked, and I hold it in the current until its ready to go. None of us can believe it. I walk back to the car to grab a Hen Harrier – I want a drink. On my return, I find the net. It was on the roof of the hut, obviously. I sit on the bench watching my friends cast, and I try to take it all in, enjoying a pint. I phone my wife and I feel like crying. Talk about dumb luck. Maybe every dog does have its day.

Lamont phones Davey and tells him that we are off the mark. Meanwhile, I've grown into the role of Spey hero. As we approach lunchtime, what we thought was going to be a bonanza returns to normal salmon fishing. It's soon time to migrate back to the top beat for lunch, and I can only just fit my fully plumed peacock tail into the car. My Instagram and WhatsApp posts simply show a photo of me and my fish, with the caption: *Put a Ribble lad on the Spey – second cast*! Of course, this is designed to be deliberately provocative, tongue planted firmly in cheek.

I could have walked back to the top beat on my hands, but I decide to take the car for what feels like a victory lap. As I watch Lamont and the Heron depart in front of me, there is only one track that I want to hear. If one thing inspires me to write and attempt to be creative, it's the Beta Band. I don't know why they connect with me so much, but they do. I like the films, the music, the fanzines; I like the underlying sense of humour and I like their playfulness. Man, do they fill me with a true sense that anything is possible if you try, and so what if hardly anyone gets it? For me, what you do is more important than what you gain from it, so with that in mind, I reach for their debut release, the three EPs, and select Dry the Rain. The opening lyric is, 'This is the definition of my life,' and right there and then, it sure felt like it. I had caught a salmon on the fly, on the Spey and on my first visit. I know that the only way is down from here, but I haven't finished going up. The ten-minute drive back up to the top cabin passes in a dizzying, multi-spectrum, technicolour zero gravity, and I intend to savour every minute. Sing it, shout it, feel it, 'I need love!'

Rare moment when you walk into a hut on the first morning and everything has gone ultra-right, and I am greeted by handshakes and beaming smiles as I sit down. Lamont is in full Captain mode now, explaining his generosity to an approving Davey, who I'm sure is glad to see the party up and running. I know it was a lucky fluke, so I quietly play it all down, but my outwardly glowing facial expressions are betraying me. Internally, I am moonwalking around the hut while Andy and George describe their morning. They have seen a couple of fish, but are yet to make contact.

My afternoon is spent in the grass watching Lamont and the Heron do their thing, and briefly chatting to Davey. I am intrigued to hear his story since, let's face it, most of us anglers spend years thinking about how we could possibly transform a passionate pastime into a paying gig. I've thought about it long and hard, and realised that it could just become another job, and who needs that? Davey had worked in industry before, and an injury at work meant that he had to find another way to pay the bills. He tells me how he had fished all over Scotland for pretty much anything with fins, before ending up here some years ago, and it's clear that his passion for the outdoors and angling has not diminished. I explain how I've taken a blind leap into the antiques and vintage goods game, and that I'm making it up as I go along.

'It's never easy, but it's always entertaining,' I say, and then I ask him about waders and tackle.

In umber tones, he informs that my nearly-mine Simms waders are 'shite,' and I am less than thrilled to hear this, since I've already paid for at least a leg. He goes on to say, in very plain-speaking terms, 'They're all shite. Just buy a refurbed pair off my mate, Diver Dave.'

I rather excitedly tell him that I've been up to Diver Dave's in Aberdeen, where I witnessed the magic show first-hand.

The Heron slowly wades out at the bottom of the run, and makes his way over for a sit-down and a brew. The spring sunshine on our faces is glorious, and I think to myself, *If this doesn't do it for you, you had better check your head.*

Davey departs for the bottom beat, to see how Andy

and George are getting on, leaving the Heron and I to exchange superlatives about the water in front of us. The one thing about the Heron is, he is persistence incarnate. If he was a full rod, he'd do ten hours without hesitation. I give it twenty minutes and get in at the top. The day drifts out with nothing more to report, and at 5pm we agree to pack up and head to the pub for some tea. Meanwhile, we get permission to pester the Boat Pool until dusk.

Back at the Mash Tun, the home of affordable single malts, one of the barmen tells us the tale of the most expensive whisky in the whole joint. In the back of the pub, there is a large display case filled with partially full bottles of Glenfarclas, of which a shot of the 1952 will set you back – wait for it – £1,200! It's so rare, not even the Glenfarclas distillery has a bottle. I ask if he's ever sold any.

'Oh yes,' he says enthusiastically, 'a few months ago, two American guys came in and ordered two doubles (*DOUBLES*!) and a can of Coke.'

Apparently, these philistines then proceeded to pour the Coke into these most limited of editions and necked them with gusto. Pay, turn and leave.

FFS!

Day Two

Same routine: stunning breakfast, get Noel Coward his paper, watch the Heron rise up out of bed already in his waders and free fall to the top beat. Today, I am fishing the Little Turn at the top of the top beat.

The Heron laid on his back in the sunshine, watching as I deep wade and perform some pulmonary casting into a strong gusting upstream gale; neither sight is a pretty one.

What a difference a day makes, you'd better believe it! I make a dog's dinner of it for nearly an hour, but it feels like much longer, and I slump out of the water and wander down to watch the Heron start his turn in the next pool. My Simms waders are seeping in on the sole of my right stocking foot, despite the fact that I've only worn them three times, so not happy there. I think about what a ball-ache it will be to send them back and argue the toss over a refund (on my return home, I am told that I must send them back to Simms in Norway, where they will be tested to establish if they were indeed faulty, or if I had broken them. They offer to exchange them, with a turnaround time of approximately one month), which means that I am back down squarely to earth as lunch approaches and we rotate towards the Boat Pool. The lunch interval reveals that nobody has had pull.

At 3.30pm, I am sent a photo of Andy with a fish from the Little Turn. It's the single greatest photograph of a salmon that I have ever seen. The fish, a twenty-one-pound silver bullet of a springer, is being cradled in the water by an ecstatic Andy. It's absolutely massive, and so silver that it's almost blue. We go for a victory meal in the Aberlour Hotel. No more fish are caught that day.

Day Three

Breakfast, paper, waders and free fall; you get the picture. We are hitting our stride now, into the groove and moving in time to the music of the week. The Heron and I are left in charge of the top hut for an hour and a half. We make a brew by turning on the brass gas tap that's connected to a camping hob, and sit on the bench in front of the hut while drinking our tea. I look at the Heron and he looks at me.

'Did we remember to turn the gas off?' I ask, as I jump up and dash back inside.

'Fuck me, Boo (my nickname), you only had one job,' he says, while lighting a roll-up in the doorway. 'Don't blow the hut up.'

The gas *was* off, but this scene has broken us, as we have both automatically pictured the roof blowing sky-high and the two us looking as though we've been fired out of a canon, before explaining to a rightly distraught Davey that we accidentally destroyed his hut. This mental image, along with our subsequent role play, has us bursting into a sustained fit of the giggles for the next hour.

Lamont and George have both had fish this morning from the Boat Pool. In each case, the fish were in stunning condition and weighed in at around nine pounds each.

Evening meal, whisky, turbo big wine, etc. Back at the cottage for lots of laughter and checkmate cheese board. Noel Coward ascends to his Captain's quarters and asks us to keep the noise down.

It's been intriguing to watch Lamont throughout the week, especially on the odd occasion where I've caught him check himself before he wrecks himself by not expressing an opinion or telling one of his tales from his not-so-distant past.

The Heron and I are in our single beds, sheeted up (Lamont's turn of phrase for being pissed early: 'I started with a pint at 1pm and was sheeted up by six!'), properly drunk and still laughing about not blowing the hut up.

Day Four

Breakfast, Coward, paper, waders, etc. Lamont gets another from the Little Turn, while George and Andy each get one from the top beat. I'm ready for home now. I miss my wife, my children and even my dog, Sweep. I am a true home bird; I have never been anywhere that I haven't been glad to leave. That Includes many countries in Europe, as well as the USA. Don't get me wrong, I have enjoyed some superb experiences and met some beautiful people, but get me the fuck home every time.

Evening meal, couple of beers and the motherload of cheese (the Formula One of food: do it long enough and it's going to kill you), but there's less wine in the cottage now, so it's early to bed. We can stay until Sunday, but I'm away early Friday morning; the pull of family is too great, and I can't bloody wait to see them and give them all a massive squeeze.

All has been fine while I've been away, with my wife and kids insisting that I should stop here until Sunday, but the simple fact is that I don't want to. This trip has been one of the best weeks of my life, and I hope to be invited back again next year. If, however, I am never allowed to return, I will cope. I suppose that's the point of getting away from time to time. You get a chance to reflect on what you already have, which usually means realising that you're fortunate enough to have already scored a massive bullseye.

Day Five

Home.

5

Bandit Country

I turn cautiously and slowly look over my right shoulder. My left eyebrow arches sharply upwards, while both my senses and my eyes widen. What is on display could easily be a scene from either *Mad Max* or *Grand Theft Auto*. These are signs of rebellion, or perhaps alienation from a broken system of neglect, which helped produce a golden generation of quick-fixers, clickers and media dopers, hooked on the hit of instant gratification. Black and grey smoke clouds billow and swirl throughout the woodland, emanating from two separate sources in between the large, angled and gnarled broadleaf trees. One is a small bonfire made up of large branches, while the other is the crash site of a totalled scooter, following some obviously failed stunt.

This tribal gathering is taking place at Melling's Wood, Preston, on the Ribble. The soundtrack accompanying these images is provided by the hissing, pressured screams and ratty, stuttering moans of two moto-crossers and one as yet un-torched scooter being razzed through the wood by various colourful scamps. With the smoke, the noise, the fading light, the colours, the three horsemen of the apocalypse and the leaping, flickering flames, it's like fishing during a riot. I'd like to see this image on the cover of the next issue of *Trout & Salmon*, but as much as I want to take a photograph, I'm concerned that the flash may draw their attention.

Over the years, I've spoken to anglers who deal with this bandit country by being armed with such weaponry as pepper spray, illegally imported CS gas and even knives. The police and the environmental agencies have long since given up coming down here at all, and I'm sure they're pleased with how the tactic of a managed decline, no doubt Xeroxed from the government's considered blueprint for the North West, is working. This method is nice and cheap, and comes with the added bonus of drastically cutting down on paperwork. My own strategy is to maintain a stealthy, non-threatening, low-profile state of semi-invisibility, but it's a hard trick to pull off. I try and fish passively, like Gandhi might have, only with Stan Laurel's facial expressions. As Ray Charles so wonderfully sang, 'The night time is the right time to be with the one you love,' as long as the one you love isn't going to napalm you in your waders, using a molten fountain of scorching Vesper oil.

Another tactic is to never fish this fun palace alone, and instead buddy up with somebody who's a slower runner than you, or even better, a slow-moving non-swimmer. Pick your buddy and never *ever* let the buddy pick you. If you're asked by anybody if you'd like a day salmon fishing on the river, don't ask '*Where?*' ask the bastard *'Why?'* and then run your internal checklist for a quick health diagnostic of potential weaknesses. Only accept the offer if you're one hundred percent bushy, while they've had a recent surgery on something like hip, knee or heart (HKH). Keep this acronym on a constant loop of self-preservation. *HKH* is the mantra, do not forget it. *You* pick the buddy.

'Hi Peter, how's the knee? I hear surgery went well. How're you fixed for a quick guerrilla hit-and-run in Melling's? Apparently, it's holding fish... No, no, it's miles better than it used to be. We (I) will be fine.' Now, I'm not saying that Hypothetical Peter is merely bait in this scenario. I'm sure he's cracking company, so we'd be in for some immensely fun times, but if shit were to turn real, it's lovely to have him there as an unsuspecting insurance policy while you nimbly flee through the *Ninja Warrior* woods.

Unsurprisingly, this beat doesn't have a waiting list, since it's so far off the charts in Chinese airspace (what my close angling companion, Lamont, calls anywhere that you aren't meant to be). It lost its charitable status in the early nineties, when the now defunct Preston Centre Angling Club ran out of good Samaritan, un-assaulted bailiffs. The opposite bank was a brief sanctuary, until the fateful night when a laser dot beamed from the woods drifted down a sea trout angler's face and chest, denoting either a laser pen or gunsight, you decide. The red dot had produced an unbearable ennui in said angler, who called it a night. Nothing spreads so gleefully as bad news, and from there, the word was out that the place had finally gone feral. You can occasionally still be asked to pay for a day ticket by somebody claiming to be the beat's bailiff, but this payment isn't so much for a permit as it is a blunt request for protection money. After all, you wouldn't want to have your car done over, or for some unfortunate accident to befall you. This pizzo is a cousin of the classic matchday parking tickle, 'Give us a fiver to mind your car,' employed by street-savvy children living near football grounds, which, incidentally, was only £1 for twenty-odd years, but now they're looking for notes. I blame Sky. It's *all* about the money, baby, as Ray 'bet now!' Winston will tell you.

Fari vagnari u pizzu is Sicilian for wetting one's beak, and in Melling's Wood, there are many beaks all on the ultimate zero-hour contract. They took David Cameron's call for a Big Society and ran with it, and who could blame them? Make the most of your natural resources, I say. In fact, isn't that Eton's Latin motto, secretly embroidered on the inside pocket of their blazers? *Fari vagnari u pizzu*, like an ancient mission statement.

By now, I expect that you're getting the picture of how Melling's Wood can be a cruel and savage place, but – and now here's the rub – it's tidal, and there can be a build-up of fish in low water. So, what's a terminal chancer like me to do? Bleat that there's no rain, preventing the fish from getting up to our wonderful, protected club beats? Well, the salmon can't hail a cab or get out and walk; they must sit tight and wait it out, which is why I'm here, fishing alone like a blacked-up, dark ops Martin Sheen, immersed in water and trying to reach Colonel Kurtz, while a petrol-powered version of *Lord of the Flies* on crack plays out behind me. Hypothetical Peter said that he didn't want to come, the lousy shitbag. My iPod is currently halfway through The Doors' The End, daylight is about to give way and it's all just a bit surreal. I'm in my absolute element here. Welcome to salmon fishing at its purest.

I've driven twenty miles to get here from my home in Clitheroe, Lancashire. I'm a member of three fishing clubs, costing a grand total of £600 per year, and I fish on every lift and sometimes on low water, but not often unless I'm shrimping. For that money, I get unlimited access to around twenty-five miles of the Ribble, making membership a total, gilt-edged no-brainer; £50 a month for endless fun. I have never really cared for the lottery of booked weeks on rivers with better salmon runs, as I can't afford the time or the money, and anyhow, this deal isn't about numbers caught, it's about spontaneity, graft, craft and the chase. The treasure is in the hunt and the hunt is the treasure.

I've tailored my life around the river. I gave up a soul-sapping job in education (which I now refer to as the cracker factory) and took the plunge, which was in no way an easy decision. I'd been employed continuously from the age of sixteen until I was forty-seven, before diving headfirst into self-employment with no safety net beyond my voluntary redundancy money. I now deal in antiques, art and decorative interiors from a pitch in an antiques centre in Preston. The best part about this set-up is that the centre is staffed, so I don't always have to be there, and it's open seven days a week. I just drop new stock off and get the hell out of there, back to the river. *Happy hens lay more eggs*, and all that. In spring, conditions permitting, I fish before and after work. I'm lucky, but at the same time, you make your own luck. When there's no action on the river, I concentrate on acquiring stock, painting and writing. Financially, we just about manage, but it's work-life balance that's important to us (my wife and I), so there's no commuting, no meetings, no other people's agendas – fuck that shit. I gratefully take my kids to and from school every day, which I regard as a total luxury. Family and work balance are key. If those jewels are glowing, it makes everything else easy, and life becomes a self-nourishing, flowing circular movement.

Sorry about that little meander off topic, but I just wanted to give you a slither of background.

To prise a salmon out of Melling's, you really need to spin with a touch of water on, or use shrimp on low water under a float, as most of it curves under the wood in a deep arc and is too slow to carry a fly. At the top of the wood, it bottlenecks, and this is where you fish the fly in the quicker water. You can cover the width of the river here, so that each cast flows round with a nice left-to-right swing, creating an ambitious sense of inner optimism. My fly choice is always local favourites on small doubles, i.e. the Verminator and the Black Shrimp fished in tandem. I fish these as they are tried and tested by Ahab, my Yoda of the catchment, who has been at it obsessively for fifty years now, so he knows the dance.

Ahab is almost completely bionic these days, thanks to hip, knee, shoulder and stomach operations. He would make a wonderful Hypothetical Peter, but unfortunately his Melling's days are firmly behind him, due to him having a top speed of Marmite. 'I can't put up with that shite anymore,' he hissed at me recently, twisting his tanned and wrinkled face while rubbing his neck (he reminds me a bit of a leathery old tortoise). He talks wistfully of the late eighties and early nineties, vigorously croaking out numbers like a bingo caller with Tourette's. 'Twenty-eight! Twenty-eight! Twenty-eight between three of us in eight hours!' These aren't embellished flights of whimsy, spat out by some bullshitting balloon, either. Salmon was the analogue forerunner to crypto currency for nearly every angler on the catchment to swap, trade or sell. Two salmon could keep you in best bitter for four days. Indeed, I once watched, open-mouthed, as Lamont swapped a recently deceased tiger trout for salt and pepper spareribs and wings in a Blackburn takeaway. He placed his order first, and then produced the trout out of a plastic carrier bag, rabbit from a hat-style. It was touch and go for a few tense, uncomfortable seconds, until the silence was finally broken and the transaction was approved, proving a tiger trout to be more spendable than Bitcoin, in Blackburn at least. Those days have firmly been put to bed, though. Here and now, the Ribble is ninety-eight percent C&R. Yes, the bullet that is compulsory catch and release is in the chamber, and the safety is well and truly off. We are just waiting for it to be fired now, even though our annual run of salmon has gradually increased over the last three seasons.

If I don't catch a fish in this brief session, it won't be because of the flies or my tactics, both of which have been proven successful many times. Here's how I line up for today's hit-and-run: thirteen feet of 2011 Vision Catapult, Greys Xflite reel, Snowbee 2D full floater with 10-feet slow sink tip and Seagar fluorocarbon (23lb to 19lb). Apart from changing sink tips and very occasionally using an integrated sink tip line, that's me; the only thing I buy annually is the fluorocarbon. Two small, untidy fly boxes kept in my ancient Barbour A970 Spey jacket complete this minimalist portrait, in accordance with my strict rule to replace only when broken. The run that I am currently wading down is only forty metres in length, so I will go through it twice and leave. If the light wasn't fading, I'd fish a couple of more runs on the way back to Clitheroe, but alas, I'm running out of wriggle room.

With the sun and the smoke both subsiding in equal measure, and the *yoofs* calling time on their merry little demolition derby, I climb out of the river and head up the bank towards the car. I'm soothed by the gentle chords of a sitar on Dave Pike's track, Mathar, as I confidently stride out while quietly hoping that I won't be mown down by a stolen motorbike. The juxtaposition of all these elements ignites my inner glow, and my smile blooms like cherry blossom. These blissed-out moments are to be cherished, for they are habitually brief. Speaking of which, my phone rings. It's Lamont.

'Everything's just gone nuclear in Chinese airspace,' he spits out breathlessly.

Allow me to walk you through the edited highlights of our conversation:

The tale begins with an 'idiot on eBay.' Lamont wanted to blend in with the locals, so he thought it prudent to buy a disguise in the shape of a vintage 1992 purple Reebok shell suit. Once the track suit arrived, he planned to fish behind the Tickled Trout Hotel, on their £10-a-day beat; pay at the petrol station and fly, shrimp or spin. However, Lamont didn't like paying, as he could only have an hour at a time due to work commitments. He figured that if he looked like he was just out for a walk, he could stash a rod and fish when the coast was clear. Lamont likes this spot; he has recently caught three salmon in four hours and lost another two on a paid day ticket. So, the purple pillock was happily spinning far down the bank, hidden in the undergrowth of balsam, when he heard two voices. They were apparently looking for a man in a purple track suit, who had been spotted with a rod. This they had deemed suspicious, as they hadn't sold any day tickets.

Lamont was using a twenty-year-old, eleven-foot MacMartin salmon spin special, Shimano bait runner, 30lb Berkley FireLine to 15lb Maxima and a black 15-gram Spintec flying C. He was wearing a full purple polyester and nylon mix Reebok shell suit.

Upon hearing the voices, he immediately flung

himself headfirst, complete with rod, into the tallest balsam and thickest brambles, allowing himself no more than an inward scream as his new garment provided little or no protection from the thorns, thistles and nettles. The two men were barely ten feet away up the bank, stood on a slight raised overhang on the edge of the carpark. During the course of their conversation, overheard in its entirety by the cringing Lamont, they ran through a list of candidates for the probable perp, based purely on how the poacher had been dressed. These included:

An Eastern European, possibly Polish
A scally from the nearby council estate
A member of the travelling community
An Eastern European scally from the nearby council estate, who had been evicted from his caravan

They had excluded out of hand the possibility that the perpetrator was a tight-fisted, middle-aged working man with a narrow IQ. Lamont lay there, frozen in fear and shame, for two hours until, under the cover of darkness, he was sure that he'd be able to escape back to his car and scurry home. On this occasion, he had just about managed to climb out of his self-dug hole with all of his limbs intact, yet strangely enough, he felt vindicated by this leisure suit episode.

'The outfit did its job and threw them off the scent,' he declared triumphantly. 'They joined all the dots using their preset stereotypes, and besides, it's *very* comfortable.'

His twisted moral compass is trying to somehow manoeuvre him up onto the moral high ground, and all I can think about is how I wish that I'd have phoned him while he was hiding. Imagine that!

The Ribble makes certain demands of an angler, and these are amplified for the salmon chaser. You must establish your pain threshold early, because you don't fish the Ribble, you go fifteen rounds with it. The Ribble is Robert Plant screaming the intro to Immigrant Song; it's Tina Turner belting out Nutbush City limits; its Guernica in waders. So, if you think you're going to casually rock up for twenty hours a season and simply catch a salmon, and then bitch about it when you don't get close, you had better change your definition of disappointment.

If, however, you can suck it up and maybe catch ten in a hundred visits across the season, and can handle living in a sadomasochistic state of being permanently on-call without losing your shit, there are riches awaiting the worthy. Everything becomes both richer and sharper as you exit the world of the counted and measured, and then, and only then, will we say, welcome to the majors. You made it.

6

Union Gap: Witness the Shitness

OK, so I've given you a snippet of my voluntary redundancy from the cracker factory story, but I feel like you deserve the benefit of full disclosure. Here goes something.

The cracker factory was looking to cull a section of its workforce in the name of creating an improved, more streamlined service, which in turn lowered both morale and standards to a noticeable degree in the space of twelve months. I had heard plenty of whispers about deals being made with inept managers, which included nice fat payoffs to get them off the books. This was the narrative that rattled around my mind when I found out that my voluntary redundancy request had been accepted, despite the fact that after sixteen years' service, Human Resources couldn't provide me with a copy of my contract. Understandably, I feared that this was the first step on the road to stitching me up.

A meeting was scheduled, where I would meet the head of HR to negotiate a severance package (typically, a week's salary for every year of employment). I needed representation from the union, but my rep was about as much use as my dog Sweep when it came to the first round of negotiations. He already had his eye on protecting his own job, but fortunately, I still had round two to go.

At this point, it was time to enlist the help of a big hitter; the only man in Britain to successfully earn eighteen points on his licence without being disqualified from driving. Lamont had walked into the magistrate court with a sob story and performance worthy of an Oscar. Representing himself, he used what became known in legal circles as the 'Dog and Dad' defence, arguing that the only reason he had been speeding was because he had a badly injured dog in his car, while at the same time, believe it or not, his father was being rushed to hospital after suffering a heart attack. Add into that heady mix a pregnant wife and four children, all at different schools, and it becomes an intoxicating walk on the wild side. Both incidents were indeed true, but had occurred months apart. In the end, the magistrate decreed that Lamont could continue to drive, due to the erroneous circumstances surrounding the offence. After the defendant withdrew from the chamber, the recording clerk was heard to comment that she'd never seen anything like it.

I had found Lamont sipping a coffee and loitering behind the Tickled Trout Hotel, just outside of Preston, and the blank expression on his face suggested that he was revisiting the harrowing experience of his shell suit fiasco, having been returned to the scene. I outlined my needs in clear and basic terms. I had been offered

£7,000 in redundancy, but I wanted to attempt to up that figure to whatever I could get.

'Either you give the orders, or you take them,' he said, nodding sagely. 'Yeah, baby, let's spin this wheel.'

Looking back into the vapour of that time, I now realise that he had been binging on a boxset of vintage episodes of the seventies cop show, *Kojak*. I might have figured it out sooner, but he distracted me with a theory about most HR 'raptors' being failed dentists. 'They like to dish it out, but they can't take it,' he explained.

For some reason, I'm reminded that he once had a first date at a public swimming pool. He tried to impress the girl by demonstrating how long he could hold his breath underwater. I know, I know, there are several questions that remain unanswered, but I can tell you that there was no second date.

Anyway, the big day rolled round, and I met Lamont in the pub at midday (the meeting was scheduled for 1pm). Several of my colleagues had already been through the procedure, and the standard deal was a week's pay for every year and to finish in six months' time. There was also a 'no revolving door' policy, which meant that you couldn't apply to return within a two-year period after accepting a payout. Lamont looked the part in a nice two-piece black suit, white shirt and black tie; his funeral outfit. Ordering a pair of pints and two large whiskies, he laid out his plan.

'Let them talk first, and then tell them that you won't go for the amount they're offering.'

Bulletproof.

The Head of HR was sat in a dimly-lit back office, and after ushering us in, she quickly outlined her position and produced some paperwork for me to sign. I then turned to see Lamont taking the cellophane wrapper off a lollipop, Kojak-style.

'You may need to rewrite those documents,' he shook his head. 'It's the offer. It's no good, see. We know that you've been cutting deals to pay off ugly ineptitude. You guys are all the same – you want the fruit, but you don't want the skin. You want to use them up and wear them out.'

Has he just used lyrics from a late-seventies Odyssey record? I thought, feeling the temperature rise as he leaned back confidently in his chair.

Already, Mrs HR was way beyond any words. She simply stared blankly at him for a few awkward seconds, before finally saying, 'I'm not sure that I know what you mean. It's a perfectly reasonable and standard offer. Do you have another figure in mind?'

Lamont rolled the lollipop around in his mouth and answered – wait for it – 'That's right, sister. You got it.'

This is all happening in Blackburn, Lancashire, by the way, and not New York City, NY.

Lamont took a folded card out of his jacket pocket and slowly slid it across the table. I had no idea what was written on it.

She opened it up, and I saw her eyes widen in alarm, as she read the note and then asked, 'You want twenty-eight thousand pounds?'

I wanted to punch his head off his shoulders.

'Yep,' Lamont confirmed, 'my client has been made to feel like a pantomime villain throughout this whole process, but, twenty-eight-K and he's gone today, baby, and he'll sign whatever the hell you want. You can then get on with conning the next poor sap who walks through that door.'

She stood and politely informed us that the meeting was over.

Outside, Lamont grinned and told me, 'She'll be on the blower before you can blink.'

Two days later, I gleefully accepted £7,000, offered on the proviso that I signed a contract stating that I couldn't return to the cracker factory for a record-breaking five years, and I also had to work a bastard six months' notice.

I'm now recalling some of Lamont's other notable negotiation techniques. He once demanded a meeting with his own boss, to ask for a pay rise.

'How much do you want, Lamont?' the boss asked. The answer was £45,000 per annum.

'Well, I suspected that you were going to be after a pay rise,' the boss said, 'so I've been through your file, and I've got good news, Lamont. You already earn forty-six thousand pounds a year, but don't worry, I don't want you to take a pay cut. Is there anything else that I can help you with?'

Shortly after the salary incident, Lamont suffered the ultimate shame of fitting a company tracker to his company van, putting paid to untold off-the-grid river excursions.

Kojak, though? WTAF?

7

Sensations in the Dark

Part One

Sea trout fishing at night. Which bright spark thought of that? Whenever I read about it, the narrative is always the same. Magical evenings spent under sumptuous, velvet, indigo skies, chasing silver ghosts while the rest of the country sensibly sleeps.

Have you recently been mis-sold a fishing experience? If so, you could be owed a vast sum in compensation!

Let's be honest, it's not normal behaviour, and in my experience, it *always* ends badly. For instance, last year I gave it a go and caught a bat (I'm still traumatised after the unhooking), and this year I have again been hopelessly groping around in the dark, tripping over and bumping into various species of stinging plants while trying to unearth this arcane magic. Maybe I'm just falling at the first hurdle and should be more persistent, or perhaps I'm just shit at it. Either way, for me it's invariably been a fruitless leap into a gravel pit of sorrow.

Two years ago, I accidentally set off an infrared

farmyard alarm system, designed solely for the purpose of stopping you from abandoning the magic at 4am. It was not what I would describe as a pleasant experience, caught frozen like a Colditz inmate under the full, brutish beam of a large spotlight. I can't tell you the fear I felt as the front door swung open to reveal a less than impressed, semi-dressed and sleepy stooped elderly farmer. I have an automatic, inbuilt fear of farmers, due to the ones I've met being total no-nonsense, weather-beaten types, calloused by relentless exposure to the elements. Literally working themselves to death, they are blunt and to the point, and I'm yet to meet one over sixty who can stand up totally straight, so gnarled are they by the twenty-four-seven workload. I do my best to give them a wide berth and avoid doing anything to irritate them. My quest to catch a fish doesn't register as so much as a blip on their radar. To them, I'm just some invasive species to be begrudgingly tolerated, completely green to the harsh realities of their world.

'You'd never catch a farmer in accident and emergency,' Lamont once wisely stated.

The dressing-down I received was a thing of terrifying beauty. I had never witnessed anything quite like it. He exhaled a sonic blast for at least four minutes straight, visibly turning a high blood pressure shade of Merlot as he gave me both barrels in a tongue-lashing that was so forcefully delivered, I had to turn my grimacing face to soften the impact. With his thick-cut, crooked fingers, he kindly pointed me in the direction of a red-painted sign that looked like it had been scrawled by a mangled, blood-soaked claw, and which clearly stated that if you are still on the river after 10pm, you couldn't leave until the alarms were turned off at 6am. My bad, as they say.

At that point, I would have gladly paid to leave. The long pool that I had chosen to concentrate my efforts on, expecting it to burst forth with life after the sun had gone down, remained silent and motionless. Meanwhile, the heavens had opened, and a month's rain fell on me in the space of twenty minutes. Resigned to my fate, I continued on resolutely down the pool, trying to mimic the winning tactics I had read about. I was going to keep running until sunrise, nobly stoic in my endeavours while the rest of the foolish world slept to the beat of the same old song. Unlike them, I was free, living life with two fingers firmly up in defiance. Or was I just another prick with a fishing rod?

One thing that really stands out at night is the choral sound of the nocturnal. Everything seems to be in a state of high distress, with only eerie shrieks, shrill barks and loud, anguished screams to be heard. Slowly, this battle between the hunters and the hunted wears you down to a twitchy, raw, bare nerve. Add to this the sound of undergrowth moving and snapping branches, and you start to run through every horror film you've ever seen, all the while frantically calculating how far from the secure unit you are as the crow flies, or wondering if the authorities had caught the escaped murderer from a nearby prison. This soundtrack is punctuated by an internal dialogue that tells you to get your shit together, before reassuring you that you're having a great time. Then, you hear some medium-sized mammal loudly screaming out like it's being viciously disembowelled.

Turning to the bank to switch on my head torch and change my homemade, ham-fisted Useless tied fly (that's its name, the Useless. There are a couple of variants, such as the Completely and the Totally), I found myself almost nose-to-nose with the owner of two bright red eyes that were looking directly at me. After this encounter of the deer kind, I nearly soiled and jumped out of my waders simultaneously. *Fuck this shit,* I thought, *I'm off!* I was forty-nine years old, which is stent season for those of us who are carefully managing our departure from this earth by eating and drinking just enough cheese and wine to fend off old age by dying before it's too late to remember your loved ones; trapped, scared and unconsciously becoming a burden to your family. I wasn't going to pop my clogs there, though, alone by the river in the dark, blanking! I'm aiming for around seventy-two, which gives me at least another 8,395 days if I can stay lucky.

With all of that in mind, you'll understand why, by the time I was finally allowed to exit the farmyard, my fortitude was in tatters. I was broken by a combination of evasive sea trout, nature, the elements, a high-tech alarm system and a sleep-deprived farmer who made the shark from Jaws look like a playful Labrador puppy.

It's June 2019, and I'm bravely spinning on a big water with Ahab, during a lovely impromptu afternoon session on the stunning River Hodder. *This is more like it,*

I think, feeling like Snow White singing to all the happy critters in the woods.

Ahab and I had peered over the Hodder's high bridge to assess our prospects, and I had concluded that there wasn't much love in the foggy waters below. Ahab, on the other hand, had said that he liked it, and suggested that we should at least go through both pools once.

'There could be a diamond in that darkness,' was how he'd put it.

For my part, I'm angling for little more than a couple of mid-afternoon pints, but if he thinks it it's worth a go, who am I to disagree?

I rarely get to fish with Ahab, but today I'm doing so purely out of plain necessity. My wife has finally passed her driving test at the ripe old age of forty-seven, and is gleefully flexing her newfound independence by taking the car out for the day. *Be careful what you wish for*, I might have cautioned my slightly younger self, having not considered the consequences of encouraging her to keep on having lessons.

Relieved of my vehicle, my options were as follows: Go old school and tie my rod to my bike with shoelaces, fill my pockets with secrets and stuff my waders into a backpack, and pedal in my wading boots.

Public transport. I still carry pained memories of being thirteen on a crowded bus with my basket, keepnet and seventeen-foot telescopic roach pole, which extended sharply to its full length, nearly skewering my fellow travellers into a living kebab. Even more agonising was the same question being posed by every elderly passenger: 'Have you been fishing, love?' Yes, of course I fucking had.

Utterly beached, I was delighted when Ahab phoned and offered to take me out to the river. Having been doing most of my fishing solo of late, usually during stolen early mornings and evenings, I'm glad of the company. It's always good to share the collective wave of optimism, collate information and join the dots of river activity, confirming each other's catch reports. It's also a joy to pick his brains and just watch him, as he methodically dissects a pool and defies all medical science by continuing to breathe.

I first encountered him about twenty-odd years ago, when I was dashing through a deep bend on the Ribble at Preston, known as Church Deeps. His only remark was that I should take my time, and I'd liked how he looked that day: small game bag slung over his shoulder, Barbour wax cotton wading jacket, Ocean rubberised waders, plaid shirt, Gye net on his back and Daiwa rod rigged for float fished shrimp, with a permanent roll-up in his mouth. I came out while he slowly fished through the pool and then exited and wandered off downstream, like a phantom. It's funny what you warmly remember about these brief chance meetings with total strangers.

We make our way by skirting around the edge of a beautiful jade field for about seven hundred metres, to what is the top of our beat. The pools that we are going to fish are the Farm Pool (it's behind a farm) and Anderton's (no Idea). Anderton's is a real jewel. It's just one of those places that fills your soul and raises your senses; the Hodder runs over the bedrock and it's shrouded by trees on either bank.

At the head of the Farm Pool, you get the feeling of being enclosed. It also runs into Anderton's, so you start there and fish all the way through both of them. We are bathed in a translucent, dappled yellow summer light; in this short journey, we have moved far away from 'real' life. I take a seat in the tall grass as Ahab goes down first; there's no need to wade, as we're both spinning and can cover the water easily. If anything, the water seems more coloured now than it did on the bridge, and his lop-sided, crablike gait is perfectly harmonised with the undulating bankside. Now aged seventy-one, a series of hip, shoulder, stomach and knee ops have taken their toll on him, but he can still cast a ten-gram flying C across any pool. The river is bolting through at a decent pace and bringing the spinner round nice and quickly. We are both silent, each quietly engrossed in our own small worlds. Taking time to actually notice things seems to be a rare treat these days; time is tight. Most of us are perpetually occupied and don't seem to be present in the now very often at all.

After giving Ahab a ten-minute head start, I get in the Farm and begin to fish. I'm using a fifteen-gram silver bullet with a red latex tail, and after going through without incident in about twenty minutes, I slowly start in the top of Anderton's. Ahab is halfway down, and his rod is bent into a fish. The tip of his rod jerks violently and the line goes slack. He looks up at me and grimaces while nodding; he looks a bit like Silvio from *The Sopranos*. His facial expression says that it was a decent fish and, encouraged, I cast my bullet over to a fallen tree and feel it coming round as I reel in, admiring the arc of my line.

Bang! I'm in. Nobody is more surprised than me. The fish moves off upstream, and it feels very strong as it surges into the mid-current, staying deep. In this veritable chocolate milkshake, it's impossible to get a look at it, but this is serious time now, so no mistakes; I keep tight. Getting over the fish, I hold it in the current in front of me, slowly cranking up the pressure until I can slide it into the net. My first appraisal had been an excited shout to Ahab that it was a good fish with a capital G, and he has now scuttled up to be on my shoulder.

'Take your time,' he croaks, repeating his advice from two decades past.

It is a thrilling contest, and now it's time to see what I've caught. The fish is ready and turned on its side as we slide the net under, and Ahab and I are equally astonished to see a brand-new, silver four-pound grilse, still with its longtail sea lice. It's a very big ask these days to get a salmon from the Hodder, and even then, it's only ever at the rear end of the season, usually October. Ahab gets in behind me after some quick photos and an almost instant unhooking, describing my catch as a 'rare' fish. I am stunned into a deep state of disbelief, while at the same time totally elated. *Who'd have thunk it?* I continue to cast and step for another five minutes, until

I reach the spot where Ahab lost his fish. As I retrieve the bullet and start to lift the rod, I spot a massive boil in the water as a fish goes for the lure. Jolted into action, I take a couple of steps back up the pool and cast again. This time, as the bullet comes round, the fish hits it with a real wallop.

Standing trancelike, I can't bloody believe it. *What kind of twisted shit is this?* The fish bolts upstream and across to the far bank, and is still taking line at a violent rate. Tightening my clutch, I get it back into midstream and babysit over it, waiting for it to go again. I don't have to wait long, as the fish shoots back over to the far bank, this time in a downstream arc. Again, I get it back to the middle, and this time I'm not letting it move. Ahab is ready with the net, and I calmly slide in a crackerjack of a sea trout. At approximately seven pounds, it is without doubt my biggest ever. In a foggy, punch-drunk haze, I tell a gleeful Ahab that I can't believe it, as he gives me a hearty handshake and tells me that I may well have 'the touch.'

'The touch' really is the phrase of high praise, reserved for describing that one angler we all know, who just always manages to do the business. It's flattering to hear, and my ego is doing handstands, but deep down inside, I know I'm not that guy, and so does Ahab.

We give it another thirty minutes, but it's all quiet from there. I am now in full scheming mode, planning ways to fish this pool at night. A seven-pound sea trout appearing on a nine-foot, single-handed, seven-weight fly rod in the dark would definitely push me up the waiting list for a stent, as my heart bursts through my chest at midnight. We walk off, and I know that I'll be back for a nocturnal visit as soon as the water level falls.

The Hodder comes up again three days later, after another downpour mimicking previous the conditions, so I sneak back after wolfing down my tea and asking if I could borrow my own car from Driving Ms Daisy, and have another bash in Anderton's that results in another small grilse.

WTAF?!

I join a procession, getting in the pool behind two other anglers who had just spun through it when I'd got lucky. One of them is super traditional, with flies in his deerstalker and a wax jacket, while the other is rocking a baseball hat with a host of tired-looking wet flies in it. It's this second fella who chucks out the line, 'Are you the guy who wrote that book?'

This Isn't my favourite opener, because who knows how it'll pan out? I wince, turn and nod, preparing myself for the worst.

'I've written my own book,' he says, smiling broadly.

'Great,' I reply, still up a blind alley and wondering where this line of questioning is taking me.

'Yeah,' he continues, while pointing at his mate, 'it's called All the Dicks I Have Fished With.'

Tears of laughter stinging my eyes, I ask him to put me down for a copy. Both men are in their late sixties, and we have a lovely thirty minutes of tall tales before I leave them to it, safe in the knowledge that I'll be back in a week or so under the cloak of darkness to try my luck with the fly rod.

Part Two

There's always a spark that lights the flame, a wild place to stoke the soul and the chance of excitement is all it ever takes. Fuse lit, I find myself rooting through tackle in the cellar, trying to find just the right balance of old gear that may do the job without me having to order any more. In all those old books, they managed their fair share of fish, despite the angling market and the quest for profits suggesting otherwise. They like to instil a sense that you are being left behind in a race for success. Well, fuck that shit.

I grab my twenty-year-old, ten-foot, seven-weight Orvis trident rod, with the Battenkill fly reel and eight-year-old dry fly line. There's no room in the budget for new gear; they'll have to do. I couple this with a phone-sized, beaten metal fly box (I like this box, because I'd like to think that it could stop a bullet while resting in my breast pocket) filled with traditional sea trout wets (Teal, Blue and Silvers) and some ancient spiders that look as though they've been on the piss with Motorhead, as well as a few battered weighted nymphs. My plan is simple: nine-foot, five-pound leader with one dropper. Sneak up just as it goes dark and elegantly catch a whopper and, finally, fully connect with the magic.

Parked on the higher Hodder bridge, sat in my boot waiting for dusk, I have a gunfighter's glint in my eye that means business. Conditions are right, and there can be no more excuses. I have open access to the river, and I need not fear any intruders from the Agriculture Club. This old rod is like a wand compared to my thirteen- and fifteen-foot double handers; the set-up feels dainty by comparison. I'm injected with a wave of optimism mixed with anticipation and tangible excitement, as I stride up the edge of the field to the top of Farm Pool. I feel focussed and ready.

My iPod is playing, and I'm listening to First Aid Kit's LP, Stay Gold. They are advising me to 'keep on keepin' on,' and life seems pretty much perfect in framed moments like this. Hopping over the stile, I slowly walk down the steps to the riverbank and hang a left, making my way towards the head of the pool. It's hard to stay out of the water and not go gung-ho and just start fishing, but for once I'm showing some restraint and following the advice of those who went before me. My only dilemma is which fly to select, torn as I am between my Motorhead rehab spiders and the eternal Teal, Blue and Silvers and gold-bodied Wickham's Fancy. I put a size sixteen Teal, Blue and Silver on the point and a size fourteen Wickham's Fancy on the dropper. Rightly or wrongly, that's my set up. My main objective is not to tangle it up on the first cast. Hopefully, casting my nine-foot leader will be well within my limited capabilities.

I've added Mucilin sinkant just out of habit, but in my pocket I've also brought a cut-down former fast-sink polyleader, which has been adapted down to two feet, in case I feel the need to get down a bit more. The fading light is just about to drop the start flag, as I make my fist cautious cast halfway across the pool. I've not got in the river, since it's more important to be quiet than to enhance how far I can cast.

As far as little brothers go, the Hodder is both handsome and sublime. It's a wild place that's not visited by many. Nature doesn't deal in straight lines, and everything formed by and blown into this river has clung to life without following the instructions. This results in an added buzz, because you know it won't give up its secrets willingly. I will have to earn any prize using guile and craft. Don't say anything.

It is with just such a cunning mixture of guile and craft that I stick my third back cast into the low-hanging branches of a bastard tree. I set-up again, same flies and same tactics. This time, though, the sport is in threading the flies without my newly acquired reading glasses. I'm still in denial about my eyesight, to which my friend and optician knowingly says, 'You must be running out of arm.' It has become an uncomfortable, frustrating and then ultimately satisfying game of chance to thread the eye of a fly, tongue out and concentration on full gas, accompanied by mild, hushed swearing.

I start over, casting out and watching my flies swing round in the current. I hear the crash splash further down the pool, as time boils down to this narrow window of heavenly opportunity. Casting again to gain another yard in distance, I'm feeling it now as it swings at a slow, controlled pace, and I have found my rhythm as I methodically repeat and move down the pool. It's a moonlit night, and if there is such a place as 'the Zone,' I am in its bullseye. Gone is the static of the mundane, the clatter of work and the tightrope of the grinding everyday routine. All of those unpleasant aspects of my life are provisionally frozen in time, and for now it's just the river and I making our own music.

I complete my run through Farm Pool and then start in at the head of Anderton's. On my first cast, I briefly hook and lose a lively sea trout of around one-and-a-half pounds; the fish taking me on the dangle in a sudden grab at the point fly. Casting again, I cover the exact same arc, slowly using a figure of eight retrieve.

Pow! A quick snatch and a surface roll, and I am playing another nice sea trout, which after a brief struggle is landed, unhooked and returned. My entire state of being is amplified, as I cover more water without any further entertainment until I enter the tail of the pool. My cast has landed squarely three quarters across the river, and the point fly, I imagine, is just drifting past the grasping branches of a semi-submerged fallen tree as my iPod soothes me with Kurt Vile singing All in a Daze Work. His gently meandering acoustic guitar almost mimics the flow of the Hodder, as my fly is clobbered by a large sea trout that steams off, running on all cylinders like a dog eagerly pursuing a tennis ball. I lift my right hand and the rod in an attempt to control the situation, but I'm just a helpless passenger as the fish goes airborne in a majestic twisting leap. I see now that the fish is approximately five to seven pounds (ish), and on its return from free jumping, it bolts up the pool towards the Farm where it leaps again, thrashing its arching body. My rod tip tells its tale and my line goes slack, and I know it's all over as Kurt gently serenades me with Lost My Head There.

Wow, holy shit, I think. *What a rush.*

I finally get it. Here, under the stars at just after midnight, I at last understand the photos I've seen of the elated faces of nocturnal voyagers, hooked on close encounters of the silver kind and driven by that moment of insanity when your arm's pulled off and your heart is reset to its animalistic factory setting.

I ain't gonna lie, I wasn't at one with the world before. I'm gutted, but not completely, and I take heart from the fact that I must have done something right. Maybe I've matured? Perhaps I've experienced growth? Nah, it was something more philosophical, I reckon.

What a wonderful, wild adventure to have; something from nothing. The night has gripped me in a way that I hadn't been expecting, giving me a slow-release feeling of warm fulfilment. As I fumble my way through the now dark fields back to the car, I begin to get a sense of the child-like magic that fuels us, a lost or forgotten simple innocence that we spend our adult lives trying to recover. It's in there somewhere, though, buried underneath a modern world of speed and contrived convenience. It's vitally important to reach in, search it out and burst the bubble to remember how it feels. The Hodder has briefly cured my amnesia, and I feel like my ten-year-old self running through the tall grass, laughing without a care in the world.

8

Strictly Business

I have been a member of Ribblesdale Angling Association (RAA) for eight years, and on the committee for five. It's a brilliantly friendly club, and I have made a lot of friends there. I had never been on a committee of any kind before, so when I was asked to become the club's secretary, I was both surprised and nervous. Fred, our long-suffering chairman of almost thirty years, put me at ease and assured me that all would be well. His experience means that he knows the history of the club and the direction it's going in, and he has intimate knowledge of the catchment area and existing membership. We have only one hundred and twenty members, the majority of whom have been at the club for over fifteen years, and there are rarely any serious problems to deal with. Occasionally, there can be the odd pollution incident, but overall, it's just standard, mundane club business.

Our meetings are held in the back room of the Swan and Royal pub in Clitheroe, and at times they make me feel like I'm sitting in an episode of *Dad's Army* or *Last of the Summer Wine*, as the potential for even the simplest of topics to ramble and meander all over the shop is incredible. Literally *any* subject can end up digressing into a downward spiral of confusion.

On the committee, we have a chairman, treasurer, membership secretary and the secretary, plus six more who weigh in like a kind of brain trust. Mostly, our agendas consist of the organising of work parties, membership applications and waiting lists, updating the website and arrangements for the annual club dinner and awards night. The youngest member of the committee is fifty, and the oldest is Chairman Fred at eighty (he accepted the role at age fifty, after being assured that it would be on a strictly temporary basis). Female representation is zero on the committee and, unfortunately, we have but one female (junior) member in the entire club, my seven-year-old daughter Rose (who caught her first trout this year!).

Lamont describes any social situation that is all-male as 'cock-heavy.'

'Went to the bar last night, but to be honest, it was too cock-heavy,' would be a typical example of its usage. It's my favourite phrase in all the world, and I try and use it wherever possible.

The committee's more lively debates often centre on determining the location of missing equipment. Here is an excerpt from the minutes of a recent meeting:

Fred: Right, we have to arrange a work party up at Nappa [Nappa is a large, unruly beat near Gisburn. It's broken into two parts and is as wild as it gets]. *We'll need a few hands, as there's a lot to do.*

John: Did we ever fix that gate lock down at Brungerley?

[Already, after one statement, we are heading downstream from the topic.]

Fred: I don't know. Boo [me], *did that lock get fixed?*

Boo: Yes, I bought a new one.

Anthony (treasurer): *Did you get a receipt?*

Boo: Yes, I'll give it you after.

John: Which shop did you buy it from? I could do with a new lock for my shed. My door blew clean off in those last gales.

[Fred starts to rub his face]

Marc: How old's that shed? The door shouldn't be blowing off like that.

John: Well, it did.

Marc: Did you self-assemble, or was it delivered pre-built?

John: I assembled it myself, why?

[Marc shrugs, and you can feel the air pressure shift within the room, as the other committee members inhale with fraying patience. It's a cold and wet Thursday night, and everyone just wants to get home. Fred attempts to reel in the conversation and get us back on track.]

Fred: We'll need all the equipment that we have. The three strimmers, fuel, safety equipment and the loppers.

Ian: I think the loppers are in Tim's boot.

Fred: Tim who?

Ian: You know, Tim – Trevor's son. I think he has the loppers in his car.

John: No, I think Tim lent them to Nigel. He had

an unruly hawthorn tree that needed aggravating. My neighbour has a nice set of extendable loppers. I could ask her?

Marc: Nigel shouldn't be using the club's loppers to cut down his own private hawthorn tree. They should all be stored centrally, so we know where they are when we need them.

Fred: We don't keep it all together, in case that place gets burgled. That way, we never lose everything at once. Remember what happened when Gordon's shed got robbed?

Marc: Aye, and then two weeks later, Gordon started a garden maintenance business.

Fred: We couldn't prove anything. John, do you think you could get your hands on your neighbour's loppers? They could be handy.

[John, Ian and Anthony exchange schoolboy glances. Fred grins and tells them to grow up.]

Ian: So, who's got our loppers again?

John: Nigel.

Fred: Could you phone him now please? We need to get to the bloody bottom of this lopper business.

[John takes out his phone, puts his glasses on and looks for Nigel's number.]

John: It's ringing.

[We all listen intently as John phones Nigel, only to be told that he did have the loppers (past tense), but that he dropped them off at Clive's, because he needed them to tackle his nephew's apple tree. Incidentally, Nigel is well, but the same can't be said of Clive's nephew's apple tree.]

John: We'd better phone Clive. He's got the loppers.

Marc: Have we written the club's name on them? Clive shouldn't be bothering apple trees with our loppers. God only knows where else they will end up.

Fred: Make a special note of that. We must be sure to write the club's name on the loppers once we get them back.

Ian: Didn't Clive leave the club?

Fred: He better not have done!

Ian: Its OK, I've found him in the club booklet. He's still a member. I'll ring him now.

[Ian proceeds to phone Clive, and casually asks him if he has the loppers. Ian gives us the thumbs-up sign while chatting away. He then gets side-tracked after enquiring about the condition of the poorly apple tree. The committee is unanimously glad to hear that Clive's nephew's apple tree is now fighting fit, and that Clive will be attending the work party and will bring the loppers.]

Fred: Thank God for that.

Me: What, for the tree or the loppers?

Fred: The bloody loppers!

Marc: We should make him sharpen those loppers. I bet he's been all over with them, playing the hero.

The highlight of these exchanges is always the body language, as exasperated and disillusioned expressions are shared by the group. Lots of fidgeting, smiling and face rubbing, as everybody realises the banality of our activities. To be fair to these blokes, though, they absolutely love the river, even more than they do fishing it. Hardly any of them get out there that much anymore, but their passion never wanes. Their burning desire is for the river and catchment to improve during their spell as the club's custodians. They have fostered a 'not on my watch' mentality that will ensure both the club and the river's safety for many seasons to come.

In some people's minds, the future of our small clubs is in jeopardy, with ageing memberships and declining salmon returns certainly cause for concern. Ribblesdale Anglers already have an eye on the future, though. We have invested in our website, making it more up-to-date and informative, as well as a one stop shop for a simplified application process. We recognise that while most of our members only pursue sea trout and salmon, the next generation of river anglers may only be interested in grayling and wild brown trout, so we stopped stocking farmed brown trout six seasons ago, and our grayling and brown trout fishing are now second to none. Our catchment is filled with exciting wild places along the Hodder, Calder and Ribble, while our Nappa beat was used as a venue during the Six Nations Fly Fishing International, July 2018. This event was a smash hit, and many of the overseas competitors were extremely complimentary about both the fishing and the wildness of the beat.

Let's face it, the culture of game fishing has dramatically changed over the last few decades. Gone is the image of the fishmonger who takes the lot, replaced by ecological anglers practising catch and release. Fish welfare – *Keep them wet!* – is their mantra, as part of an approach that is more holistic and ethical. This swing towards living in harmony with the environment, rather than acting as an antagonist who sucks what they can from it, is not only refreshing, but also crucial if we're to grow the sport. For our local clubs to survive, we must encourage and promote the joys of grayling and trout fishing. We have members who can catch thirty to forty fish in a session on three-weight rods and French Nymph leaders, and it's the attraction of this sort of wild fishing that will keep our heads above water, by enticing anglers with a fresh challenge. The key is to get people picturing a cool, rock star angler, who cares about both their environment and their quarry in equal measure.

The clubs that will be in trouble are the ones who have taken their eye of the ball and are tangled up in confusing rules (e.g. you can only spin on a harvest moon on every other leap year, on days that start with the letter T). Most Ribble game fishing clubs are populated by an ageing group of demotivated anglers, who are already thinking about jacking it in. Most of the high end, £1,000-a-year clubs built their reputations on good catch figures and premium, exclusive fly water, but even they are going to have to change the narrative and adapt quickly if they want to attract a new audience. Competition for new members is going to be fierce, and clubs that could once afford to be aloof and standoffish are going to suffer as their waiting lists dwindle and their membership slowly pops their clogs. In many cases, these places are at one minute before midnight on their own Doomsday Clock, and still they are sleepwalking into oblivion.

What's really of paramount importance is that the small, community-based clubs manage to survive, but for this to happen, them being able to retain an element of control over their own environments is essential. We have a catchment area of eight hundred square miles, covered by a grand total of two Department of Environment, Food and Rural Affairs officers, which is a big ask. As a result, it's the clubs and their members who see first-hand what takes place on the rivers, and provide reams of data that DEFRA collates and uses to inform policy decisions. Throughout the season, we monitor every aspect of the river, from catch figures, pollution incidents and extraction to the spotting of invasive species and so on. The migratory angler even pays their eighty-odd quid a year to DEFRA for the privilege of a licence fee (the cheeky bastards). However, if they do plan to make salmon fishing one hundred percent catch and release, I don't see a reason to pay a licence fee four times more expensive than that of a standard course rod.

Our catchment may not be what it once was in terms of numbers of salmon caught, but the dots have never been as joined up in the fight for its upkeep as they are now. The Ribble Rivers Trust is a superb force for good on our catchment; their ability to raise funding and use it for the overall benefit of the river system is incredible. The habitat improvements that they make, such as tree planting and fish easement, are simply stunning, and they work tirelessly to connect with the landowners, farmers, clubs and community, providing easy access to information and education alike. They boast a large base of volunteers, who all contribute to various organised projects, and in 2017 alone, they helped to plant seven thousand native trees, including oak, wild cherry, rowan, birch and field maple across four hectares in the Forest of Bowland. The new trees will provide a wide range of benefits to the environment in terms of reducing pollution in watercourses, reducing rainfall runoff from fields, providing new nesting areas for wildlife and mitigating against the effects of climate change. Their current list of ongoing projects is massive, with each completed job representing another small victory not only for our catchment, but also our communities in general.

Basically, the more folk who care, the better. Every one of us is a stakeholder in the future, after all.

9

Be a Man, Fish the Fly

Much of my fishing these days consists of a fair amount of stolen time and mooching about for an hour or two here and there; 'splash and dash' would be a good way to describe it. Thankfully, I have a few spots that are always worth a visit if I'm commuting between Clitheroe and my antiques pitch in Preston. In recent years, I have really grown into enjoying my shrimp and prawn fishing (NB, whenever I refer to shrimp fishing, I always mean both shrimp and prawn). The shrimp arrive courtesy of Ahab, who still makes the pilgrimage to Lytham St Annes to get fresh shrimp before dyeing them himself (don't tell Lamont). This allows me to fish in low water, which means that I can quickly cover a couple of beats and then get on with my day. As with all aspects of salmon angling, it's completely fruitless ninety-nine-point-nine percent of the time.

Unburdened by waders and able to freestyle in only my wellies and a waistcoat, with but a pocketful of Irish prawns from Dee at Purple Whiskers and a tobacco tin of shot, trebles and pins (I've worded that poorly. I have other clothes on, too! Jesus, erase that mental image),

I sling a net over my shoulder and carry a rod geared up with braid, ensuring maximum mobility. OK, so as a method of fishing, it's often frowned upon by fly-only purists, but that's up to them. Frown away, as far as I'm concerned, because free-lined or under a float, you won't consistently hook a fish cleaner, and that's a fact. Run it past the cognoscenti and deal with it.

On the Ribble, I'm authorised by two of my clubs to fish the shrimp, but my other club banned it twenty years ago, back when anglers were still selling fish. Now, however, with the introduction of an annual limit of one fish per angler and a ban on selling your catch, it no longer makes sense. We thought that we had a chance of getting them to let us do it again, but when the proposal to reinstate shrimp was formally brought up during our last annual general meeting, the club president said to Lamont, 'Why don't you be a man and fish the fly?' and we knew then that we were pissing in the wind. Still, it was fantastic to watch a drunk and freshly motivated Lamont then accuse the club of running an autocracy, before shouting, 'Lucius Quintius!' in the direction of the committee. Many of us on the Ribble can now be heard fondly say to anybody caught without a fly rod in their hand, 'Why don't you be a man and fish the fly?' It became an instant hit, and I take care to say it to Lamont at least once a week. It never fails to get a rise from him, usually ending in a vigorous, animated, finger-wagging rant. Light the touchpaper and stand well clear and remember that you should never return to a lit firework.

Last season, I caught more fish on the fly (five), but this year I'm struggling on the Ribble. I've fished on every lift, but I can't buy a pull. I'm not alone in this; the river is littered with broken heroes, which is why I like to be able to have a quick bash with the shrimp rod on my lunch break. I fire down to a favourite holding spot and run through it from top to bottom, which usually takes no more than an hour: perfecto! This beat also has the added attraction of a newly arrived pair of ravens nesting in the nearby woods. I've become slightly obsessed with them. They're an impressive bird to observe, and their gurgling croak call is brilliantly distinctive. Whenever they appear in the sky, skirting the wood, I'm compelled to stop and watch them. I've even found a feather (it's got to possess some kind of magic, a raven's feather, hasn't it? Yeah, it'd defo have powers).

During the second week in July, I was on my way to collect some furniture when I thought, *I'll just have a crafty mooch*. This certain spot on the lower Ribble is ideal for a quick dart in and out, as it can be accessed via a carpark not too far from the river. Sometimes, acting on a gut shot is the best shot, and I spent twenty minutes watching my trotted float while glancing around for ravens and got nothing; not an even a hint of a bob or a gurgled croak. Two anglers were two hundred metres below me, and I said to myself that I'd have another twenty minutes and then shoot off, when suddenly the float is buried and I strike...

Last year, I adapted a perfectly good Barbel rod by

cleverly cutting six inches off the butt section, making it fit my forearm and not stick in my net. I diligently painted a cork and then bunged it into the new hole and taped it up, all the while thinking that I was a genius. When I hooked a salmon, the rod exploded, and as I made a frenzied attempt at hand-winding the line and pulling the fish in, it quickly got away. Engineering and rod design, it seems, are not my strong points. Lamont regularly and rhetorically tempts my temper by asking, 'Whatever happened to your Barbel rod, Boo?' This error in judgement and intellect forced me to buy a used, nonexplosive green Greys eleven-foot Greyfelx MK2 as a replacement for my own blown to bits model. This rod is always set up in the car for the sole purpose of shrimping, and I bloody love it.

After the initial heavy *bump-bump-bump* from the salmon, I'm caught by surprise as it leaps out directly in front of me, in what is the Apollo space launch of salmon leaps, in slow motion and high definition. I'd been deep in thought about a grandfather clock that I had a chance to buy, but I forget about that now because this fish is massive.

'Oh shit – for fuck's sake,' I say out loud, eyes widening, as the fish touches down with an almighty splash and then heads off downstream, ripping line from my reel. The rod is forcibly bouncing – this fish is juiced – and all I can do is hang on as a gormless pillion passenger. As always, I begin to fanny around with my clutch, increasing and decreasing the tension like I'm working the combination on a safe. I have no control, none; it's a meltdown freak show. I'm looking around at the anglers below, and feebly trying to get their attention by waving my left arm and shouting a pathetic, 'Hey! Hey!' but they think I'm just being friendly and wave back.

FFS!

I need somebody to witness me lose this fish, as I'm totally convinced that it's about to come off. The run slows and I gain back some line before it goes again, only this time it gets further and performs another head-shaking leap. Hindsight will no doubt make this seem like a thrilling tussle, but I am truly terrified; the brute force is savage. The fish lands with a splash loud enough for the other anglers to finally take notice, and they are now slowly making their way up towards me. Both men are clearly lifelong anglers of a pensionable age, since neither of them appears to have joints and limbs working as they should, a tell-tale sign of regular exposure to the Ribble terrain. As such, it's like watching an episode of the *Walking Dead* as they amble up the bank, audibly groaning with each arduous step, and I make a mental note that both would make a fine Hypothetical Peter.

I gain some line and get over the fish, and it's now in the deep water in front of me. After surviving another surging run, I eventually get it in on its side, but I can't get it in the net. I try submerging the net square on, making it look as though the fish is going through a circus hoop, and tow it in like a docking boat. The fish enters the net like an arrow, and the mangled hook instantly pulls out, so I've got the fish scooped up, albeit it's still in the water; talk about lucky! The other anglers arrive and begin marvelling at my stunning catch.

I don't bother measuring – no time to mess around – but I can tell you that it's bloody huge, at least by my standards, coming in at twenty plus change; it could even be a twenty-three. We all agree that it's at least twenty regardless, and after a couple of quick photos, I get it back in sharpish. This is my third over-twenty in my home river in the last three years, after two decades spent trying to catch just one of the bastards. Judging by this fish's colour, it's been in our system for approximately two or three weeks, maybe less. Now, that's what I call a lunch break!

Despite my recent uptick in success, I'm still very much serving my apprenticeship on all fronts. There is always more to learn by way of greater nuances and refinements, coupled with an ever-improving knowledge of my local environment. For example, Ahab still reigns supreme with a bait rod, no question. He was schooled under the late, great Ernie Hodgkinson, who always fished with fresh shrimp from Southport, which the old Ribble boys reckon was his secret. His set-up was legendary: fifteen-foot fly rod with a spinning reel taped up at the handle with insulation tape. He used a large pike bung and he caught hundreds of fish. To hear an ex-pupil speak about Ernie is to know the true meaning of reverence.

'He could catch fish from a wet sponge,' Ahab would say of him. 'When everybody else was struggling, he'd always winkle one out. I was on the Greta one day, and he came past and had a butcher's at my set-up. He looked at my shrimp pin and then took out a pair of pliers and cut it in half. "Too long that cock," was all he said.'

Ernie was the scourge of the bottom end at Melling's Wood and Church Deeps, as well as up on the River Eden at Carlisle. He would wind up the locals by being able to get a salmon out of a seemingly dead pool, whistling while he did it. Based on what I've heard, Ernie was a real Funky Kingston, always prowling the river in his tatty old Beaufort Barbour Jacket and wellies, with an adapted fly rod and permanently dyed purple fingers. While Ernie was in his pomp during the seventies and eighties, I was graduating from being misty-eyed over ponds and Tench to becoming obsessed with fly fishing for trout on local reservoirs. As a result, I never got to meet Ernie, but he is still enthusiastically remembered by some of those older rods, who are all glowing in their praise for both his prowess as an angler and his colourful personality.

As I prance smugly back to the car, like a keenly-tuned dressage horse, and get back into grandfather clock mode, I can't help thinking how lucky I've been so far this season. *Why is it that whenever I set out with a realistic plan on above-decent water and in favourable conditions, I blank?* I wonder. Not only do I blank, but I appear to be fishing in Desolation Row. Conversely, every time I go fishing by mistake, I'm somehow showered in glittering fortune. I sure as shit don't know what the secret ingredient is, but I wish that I could bottle it.

It's now deep into September, and I still haven't managed a fish from the Ribble on the fly this season, so that's my current goal. The river has been up and down like a seesaw, which has made guessing when to fish even less predictable than normal. Rain hasn't been a problem, but getting it to stop long enough to cast a fly has; no sooner than you plan a visit do the heavens open and up the Ribble goes again. My plan is to fish above Clitheroe on our water near Gisburn. Last year, I had some luck up there on the fly rod with water, so confidence is high, and I'm hoping that lightning can in fact strike twice.

What was I just saying about plans? I'll go up there and fish 'like a man,' hoping that the Blues won't run the game, as Jackson C. Frank once sang. Maybe I should get in touch with Terry Cracking and ask him to pull his finger out.

10

Vape Expectations

Lamont and I are on one of the largest, most difficult and varied beats on the lower Ribble. It's a big old piece of water, and we have about three quarters of a mile to go at. Long pools, deep bends and shallow runs all combine to allow for several different modes of attack. There are two good runs for the fly, one situated at the top and the other located at the end of the beat. This beat will fish on most water heights, but it all fishes well if there's about ten inches on it. It's normal to have both a spinning set-up and a fly rod set-up here.

This autumn morning is almost cliché in its appearance. It's cloudy, dry and still; the trees are leafy, but there's a glaucous tone to the woods on the far bank, down to our left. We are both reclining in the grass, eating sandwiches and drinking coffee after spending the last four hours spinning, as the water is still a touch peaty in colour. We have both put a fair old shift in, and now, with lactic acid throwing a party in our backs, we are taking an hour off to recuperate. Neither of us has seen, heard or touched a fish so far, so the break is well-earned and much-needed, as hope is giving way to tedium.

Through a mouthful of cheese and ham butty, Lamont enquires, 'What time was the tide? Maybe it was too high.'

I simply lay back and stretch my toes inside my boots, attempting to resuscitate some blood cells while allowing Lamont to pursue his train of thought unencumbered by my input.

His tone is recalcitrant as he adds, 'How long does it take them to get here, four or five hours? We should be seeing something by now. Perhaps they've all gone past us? I'm convinced that the water has run off too quickly and is the wrong colour. They don't like that peat stain. Where is the gulf stream? Maybe this is one of those years where it shifts further out to sea.' He leans forward to examine the elements around us, clocking the cloud formations through squinting eyes, before ambiguously conceding, 'They don't show anymore. They all stay in the bottom of the river, where they feel safe – seals at their backs. They should be here by now. Do you think they'll come?'

Before I get the chance to answer, he springs to his feet in a rare fit of vigour and asserts, 'They should be here by now. We should be seeing fish. Maybe there are none to come? What a shit year. Seals, I've been told by an officer from DEFRA, off the record, of course. This guy was adamant – massive dent. What chance have they got? None! The counter figures are down. I bet it's the gulf stream and the nine-year cycle.

Where are they? Gone, that's where. Hoovered the fuck up by factory ships, like Pac-Man. What chance have they got? It feels empty. Do you reckon they'll come?'

He's now fumbling around in his old canvas cloth shoulder bag, which looks more suited to ferreting than salmon fishing, and produces a bottle of red wine and a neatly designed vaporizer called the Whispr Two. He then takes out his small, metal round herb grinder and starts to twist the cap until he's satisfied that it has done its intended job, before pouring the contents into the palm of his hand and filling up the chamber on his gas-powered vape. He pushes down on a button until the red light goes out, taking a large hit of the marijuana within and then passing it to me. I do the same and then pass it back, nodding as I slowly exhale. This type of behaviour is a very rare occurrence for us these days, but as we have been driven to the river by my wife, we thought we'd make the most of it. Lamont opens the wine and dispenses it in two prepacked mugs, while I unwrap a large piece of Lancashire cheese and break off a piece that he readily accepts.

Lamont gets back in the saddle, looking scornfully at the river and impulsively chattering, 'It feels deathly empty. Progressive decay. All those fuckers forty years ago, catching car boots filled with fish. All those gloating, happy landlords, smiling like toads. Nineteen eighty-three, one hundred and eighteen all dead to one rod – to one fucking rod!'

He's pacing now, as I smile and take another hit of the vape and a big swig of red.

'We should be seeing fish,' he takes a breath, shaking his head and closing his eyes. 'From feast to famine in forty years. Ahab and all his mates were like a salmon SWAT team – salmon ninjas! The temperature's all wrong – the humidity has put them down and they've run straight through. One hundred and eighteen fish to one rod in just one season. What chance did we have? The greedy wankers. Do you think they'll come? Where's Terry when you need him?'

I pass him the vape and top up his mug, and his demeanour drastically alters as he is struck by a fresh thought that he eagerly shares.

'You remember, when I was in Tibet, I stayed in an ashram for eight days?' he says. 'I had some anger issues that I needed to work through and shed, so I stayed in that ashram and spoke only to a monk named Peng. He was blissed out with life to the point of it being irritating, a real serene mother. To him, life was easy, plodding along, smiling and happily knowing nothing. He couldn't understand my Blackburn accent, but that was the least of my worries. The cheeky bastard said that my struggle was with myself, and I told him that he had no skin in the game. He had me meditating for six hours a day – self-reflection, he called it. "What you think, you will become," he'd say, fucking *Peng*. He didn't understand – he just kept going on and on about patience and kindness. Do me a fucking favour. It was as if we were from different planets. I told him about the daily barrage of bullshit, emails, bogus call centres, grifters, scam artists, bills, results and deadlines, but he had no concept of the reality that from the minute you open your goddamn eyes in the morning until you close them again at night, there is some bastard or another at you. I might as well have been talking to a brick, although Peng did say one thing that kind of made sense. "All of our problems are made by mankind," he told me.'

I do recall receiving a few irate phone calls during his attempt at finding himself in Tibet (he couldn't find himself in a broom cupboard). Most were made in a hushed, anxious voice, gasping that he didn't have long to talk. They all followed the same pattern of shrieking despondency.

'This Peng,' he'd cry, 'he's never heard of Preston, Whalley or the Ribble. I've told him about the life cycle of the salmon, but all he can do is talk back to me in riddles.'

Ah yes, it's all coming back to me now. Lamont had just about stayed the course in the ashram, before making his way back to Lhasa. He was due to catch a flight from Gonngar Airport, and had a few hours to kill before take-off, so he thought he'd visit the epicentre of Buddhist spirituality, Potala Palace. As he had made his way there, he was chopped up by a scooter cutting across him after it emerged suddenly from a back alley. His automatic reaction was to forcefully push the rider clean off the speeding scooter, sending him cartwheeling into a cluttered shop frontage while his scooter ploughed into the main street. This happened barely ten hours after his departure from the bosom of serenity, but at least he knew enough to head for the airport at once.

Naturally, he later omitted this chapter from his edited holiday journal.

I reflect on Peng's words, 'What you think, you will become,' and it occurs to me that Lamont must have thought about becoming a lethal weapon. *I bet Peng has heard of Terry Cracking*, I muse. I bet he goes by a catchy local pseudonym.

Lamont is slowing down now, and he returns to our spot in the grass before carrying on with his sermon to the sky. 'The blame game,' he mutters, 'everybody loves the blame game. The airwaves provide a constant avalanche of angst through content providers, reaction, speculation, opinion, comparison, denouncement and acclaim, twenty-four-seven. It's an exhausting wheel of bile that never stops turning. *Peng!* He had it right. It's humans always fucking it all up – the planet, the internet, smart phones, Siri listening in on your every word, so that its gaffer can sell you something and build a space mining colony. Then there are cloned cards, cookies, adverts, social media, likes, shares, plastic – everyone's demented over plastic – well, we had milkmen once! Reusable glass bottles, brought to our doorsteps every day on electric milk floats, only for the supermarkets to steal it from us and then sell it back with a red tractor on it! Surveillance capitalism, global warming, nukes, fossil fuel and the news – *never* watch the fucking news. You'll be happier for it, trust me.

'*Have you seen the fucking news*, by the way? It's a massive truckload of fear and insurmountable despair. One hundred and eighteen salmon in nineteen eighty-three, by *one* angler. No fucking wonder there are none left. Kill the brood stock and that's what you get. Sure, we blame the seals – "it's the seals, the mink, the otters and the birds!" – but we know the real answer, don't we? They killed them all for years – wiped out. It was no accident. Up on the Eden during the nineties, the Environmental Agency paid for every salmon killed. They were conducting some kind of research project, and they actually *paid* anglers for their catches. The EA put a bounty on salmon from the River Eden, like the mayor did with the shark in Jaws, all in the name of fucking data collection. Those anglers must have thought it was Christmas, running around like bounty hunters. They might as well have fired a starting pistol. There were lads booking flash holidays off the back of that initiative. We should be seeing fish by now. We should have gone lower down. I might put a Rapala on. Do you think they'll come? It must be the air pressure. This was no boating accident!'

He finishes his sermon with a fine line from our favourite film, Jaws.

I've heard the kind of primal scream that he then lets out many times before. Sometimes, you simply have to exhale the hidden anger and vent, letting it all out. Once or twice a year, my dog Sweep will sit in the centre of a field and send a lupine howl up into the sky for a few minutes. He then puffs out his chest, shakes himself down and continues with his day. I know exactly how he feels; we all do.

Similarly, this 'Where are they?' conversation is a

familiar motif that will migrate my way at least twice a year; it's inevitable. Nostalgia isn't what it used to be. Every angler over sixty-five will tell you the same tale, while they scratch their forehead in search of the answer to the missing salmon (stop scratching your head and think back to taking over ten a year for twenty years in a row). The answer, I am reliably informed, is a complex one, with many finely-balanced factors in constant flux, causing small margins and big impacts. There having been no limits on the amount of fish taken didn't help the situation – this I can agree with – however, in my brief time fishing for salmon on the Ribble, my seasonal goals have always remained the same:

1 Catch one.
2 See if I can get to ten.

I reckon that my average is something like five per season, so over the last twenty-five years, the target has never really changed for me (it's now nine years since I last took a fish). It's all down to effort; you must enjoy the struggle much in the same way an escapologist likes getting the padlocks off the sack while underwater. When you catch one, it's to be treated as a miracle.

In the time it has taken for Lamont to hold his bankside therapy session, and for us to finish the wine and the rest of our lunch, the river has dropped about three centimetres, and the colour has improved enough to suggest a realistic chance with the fly rod. Lamont goes up to the top run and I wander down to the bottom one. The time is 2pm, and we agree to meet in the carpark at five. This should give us enough time to go through each run twice.

My mood is elevated as I skirt the tall hedgerow that guides me down to the bottom run. I'm no fly-only junkie, since I don't see the need to focus solely on one method. I'm happy to fish according to the circumstances, and I'll enjoy whatever that entails. I also like the challenge of having to change tactics to suit particular conditions. This ethos allows me to get out more often, rather than be stuck waiting for optimum fly rod conditions. The low physical impact and mobility of a fly rod is a welcome bonus, though, I won't lie.

This run is located in one of those places that can seduce you with its superior aesthetics, even though, as we all grow to learn, looks can be deceiving. Considering the amount of times that I've been through it with the fly rod without so much as hooking a salmon on the fly, you'd think that I'd stop bothering. My only achievements here have been on the spinner in higher water, but while I'm hardly drowning in honey, it's still a fantastic run to fish, boasting a wide, shallow rapid section that empties into a 45m-wide pool, generating enough force to keep the fly moving at a nice pace. Down the left side of the bank are some well-established mature trees that provide great natural cover, and they also mark the starting and exit points. The riverbed fluctuates from three to approximately six feet, so, in theory, the fish may just pause before negotiating the faster shallow water, which is over 100m long and leads to the safety of a steady, slow deep pool.

Searching for some form of audio sunshine I switch my iPod on and stick it on 'Shuffle,' getting Road to Nowhere by Talking Heads. *How fitting*, I think wryly. '*Yeah*,' David sings, 'let's take that ride,' as I wade into the river. I am using a sunray shadow for the first time – blue, silver and black on a plastic tube, on a full floater with a ten-foot, fast-sink poly leader – in the belief that since I have an emphatic one hundred percent failure rate in this pool, the gamble isn't too great.

I have to say, I do like casting square and stripping back the sunray. I mix it up by letting it swing around on one cast and then stripping the next. *Who knows? Not me, that's for sure!* It takes me about fifty minutes to slowly go through the run without any hint of contact, and I climb out and walk back up to the top to sit out for twenty minutes before repeating the process. This time, halfway down the pool, I see a fish head and tail mid-current, which raises my pulse and intensifies my concentration. I fish through with a feeling of anticipation, but still without any pulls or bangs, and it proves to be just a brief, exciting interlude in the midst of an eight-hour session. I'm pretty sure that it's only the second running fish I've seen on the Ribble all year.

Then, it's enter the Leatherhead.

Walking up to meet Lamont, I run into another salmon angler who, mercifully, I only bump into once every ten years or so. Barry Leatherhead is a real glass half-empty guy, a dour, dull, toxic fun sponge, who can kill a happy vibe from a mile away. He is so negative that less than five minutes in his company is enough leave you feeling profoundly sad. Barry is about sixty years of age, but he looks much older. He has a very pale complexion that makes his sullen lips look cobalt in colour, like he's in desperate need of oxygen. Last time I saw him, he was bald, but now he has hair, and I'm struggling to take my eyes off his new rug when my phone rings. It's Lamont, calling to warn me that Barry is on his way down.

'Watch out, Barry is inbound your way,' he says. 'I think he's had his hair done, but it looks like the plugs are rejecting his head. I dived in a bush to keep out of his way. Be careful that you don't get cornered by him. He'll melt your ears off.'

This intel has arrived too late, however, as Barry is stood right in front of me, leaning on his dull-brown, sixteen-foot Bruce and Walker fly rod, which he probably bought when *The Sweeney* was a hip new TV show. Lamont was achingly accurate about his hair plugs. The last time I saw a head like this was on a malting vintage doll at a jumble sale.

Barry Leatherhead, nuclear fun sponge, the type of person who cries after sex, delivers his opening line at a snail's pace, in his dire, shrill, squeaky voice, bereft of either feeling or irony. 'Eight years since I had one on, and I lost it... why?'

He leaves a stony, silent, time-stopping, *Requiem for a Dream*-esque, cold turkey, skin-crawling void in the air, and looks at me for what feels like an eternity, making my toes curl and my arse clamp shut.

How do I respond to that? I wonder, as he takes a comb out of his waders' chest pocket. *Oh no, Barry, please don't comb your doll's head hair do. I might explode.*

Nature has come to a standstill; the river has ceased to flow, the fish aren't swimming, the wind stops blowing and the trees no longer bend. Barry's hand moves in slow motion as he tosses his head like he's in a shampoo advert, in an effort to highlight his newfound hairiness. The comb touches down and begins to plough his turnip patch thatch.

Inside my head, an atomic mushroom appears in response to one of the plugs stubbornly remaining in the comb.

'My car went in for its MOT today,' he says morosely. 'It passed, but with three advisories.'

'Oh, well at least it passed,' I answer chirpily.

I bet even his blood cells want to escape from him.

'I suppose so,' he sounds as though he's got a slow puncture. He points at my iPod ear buds and asks, 'Do you like music, then? I don't. I don't understand it me.'

This is fast becoming a medication situation, and all I can do is gaze helplessly and think about how he makes Eeyore look charismatic.

'I'm only having an hour,' he advises me in an oral tone that is coalface dark, 'I need to get home and take the lamb out of the freezer.'

Oh, Jesus.

In the distance, I can see Lamont's head peering over the hedge at the end of the field. He is pissing himself in the knowledge that I'm in Barry's soul-sapping clutches, and I can just about make out his movements as he enjoys a few more hits on the vape. Barry asks me how many fish I've caught this season, but while it's normally the highlight of any salmon angler's day to be able to modesty brag that they've actually caught one or even more, I don't have the heart to tell him that I've had four this season so far, with the biggest nudging the twenty-two-pound mark. Instead, I tell him that it's been a very difficult year, and how everyone is struggling. I even offer a get-out-of-jail theory based on the large floods we had five years ago, which left the salmon stranded as far as two hundred metres into the field. Several clubs found dead salmon on flood plains, with others discovered in puddles across the fields. It was so bad that club members were walking the catchment in their droves, trying to save as many as they could.

I can see that Barry has digested this information, and is now conjuring a suitably downbeat response. In the midst of explaining this theory, I spotted Lamont taking another large hit before vanishing behind the hedge.

'Have you seen any today?' Barry asks, oblivious to the fact that my attention is elsewhere.

Thank Christ, I think, *I have!* I triumphantly throw him a bone, telling him, 'Yes, one just showed in the run about halfway down. It won't be alone, either.'

He slowly turns and begins shuffling off in the direction of the top of the run, and I could swear that he almost smiled. I tell him that I must dash, as I'm being collected by my wife.

'It doesn't matter how many there are,' he says over his shoulder, 'I won't catch one.'

'That's the attitude, Baz,' I call softly, waving him on his way. I know he can't hear me, but he sees the wave and ambles off.

My focus switches to what has happened to Lamont. I make my way to the hedgerow and walk around it to find him lying prone, parallel to the hedge, and I immediately know what has happened. He is going through what's known in the marijuana community as a 'whitey.' Since the age of eighteen, I have had three of these; the last one happening outside the pub at halftime while watching England vs Columbia in 1998, following a quick toke of my friend's Lebanese Red Seal (I still have the scar on my forehead). I can only describe it as like being switched off for five minutes. You know it's coming about thirty seconds before you shutdown, but it's too late by then, and there's nothing you can do about it. This explains his sudden disappearance, due to his simple brain hitting the off button. He is white as a sheet, having less colour in his cheeks than Barry, but with identical cobalt lips.

'I passed out,' he sheepishly admits. 'I feel fucked. I've properly mugged myself.'

Unfortunately, there's nothing to be done other than to wait it out. There's no magic antidote that I can administer to this scuppered crab, so I just place his feet on his bag and elevate them, to try and get some blood flowing to his greedy pea brain. I sit with him for thirty minutes while he consumes a can of coke and a banana, and he starts to perk up soon enough. Thankfully, nobody else has seen any of this, allowing him to savour the one good aspect of a whitey: the feeling of euphoria when it's over. We are both laughing now, as I get him to his feet and we gingerly head back to the club carpark.

I remark that I've never read an article in *Trout & Salmon* magazine about an angler having a whitey, and Lamont tells me that it's been three years since he last used any herb. I reckon this incident will end up marking his total departure, though I remind him that it was he himself who'd brought it.

'It's a mistake to try and recreate the stunts of your youth,' he says reflectively.

Amen to that, I think, having only very recently found out for myself that age is a very real concern while playing six-a-side football at the gym. I'm fifty-one now, and nearly two-stone heavier than I was in my vibrant thirties, and still I went hurtling into a fifty-fifty block tackle with a robust, durable raging bull of a twenty-one-year-old, who went through me like I was made of candy floss. My left knee went perpendicular, leaving the leg feeling like a piece of string from the joint down. Rewind thirty years, and it would have been a contest.

At least Lamont suffered an even more unpleasant, hubris-inducing episode of 'no fool like an old fool,' when his local kick boxing club found themselves short of a fighter for an upcoming show, and asked if he could please step in for a two-round contest, purely to make up the numbers. Lamont is forty-nine himself, but he reluctantly agreed to the bout, not wanting to let the lads down. His only stipulation was that it had to be an even matchup. He phoned me up after the fight was over. It went like this:

'The lying bastards,' he raged, 'fair matchup my arse! The opponent looked like a roided-up, twenty-year-old Clubber Lang, only taller! All I did was leg it out of his way for the first round, while listening to my kids scream, "Run, Dad!" Clubber's fans, on the other hand, were shouting, "Get him, Killer!" Fucking *Killer!* Believe me, *Killer* did not want to lose to an old codger – he chased me all over. I managed to land some kicks and punches, but I was blowing out of my arse. He nearly kicked my head off at least twice. Never again.'

As we slowly wander back to catch our lift home, I can't resist echoing the wise words and sentiments of the boy Peng for a still self-conscious and groggy-feeling Lamont. 'Your struggle, my son, is with yourself.'

There must be an art to growing old disgracefully. After all, you don't want the glint in your eye to disappear completely; where's the fun in that? It's true that as you turn the corner and nosedive sharply into the bleak waters of decline, life does become geared more towards self-preservation, but it's still nice to occasionally shake the bottle, just to see if there's any fizz left.

11

The Last Dance

Lamont and I are adding up the total number of salmon fly fishing opportunities that we've had this season, as we wander up to the top of our Nappa beat. Thinking back to those rare occasions where the planets have aligned and conditions have been perfect over the past nine months, we can count five. Even by our standards, this is unusually low, although we haven't been helped by the fact that these 'perfect' days are hardly worthy of the name, so brief are they, with the river prone to rising and falling significantly in a matter of hours. I prefer to remain philosophical about it, resolving to accept that it's simply part of the cruel beauty of our chosen pastime; you never really know what you are going to get. An ability to roll with the punches is what separates those who fail from those that stay the course, but it really has been hard graft this year; the maths of it all, along with trying to work in windows to fish, have been exhausting.

Our conversation naturally drifts to the subject of cloning, and we both agree that we would need at least four copies of ourselves if we were to crack the Ribble.

Interestingly, we also both agree that our cloned selves would be better deployed on the home and work fronts, freeing up the real us to toil on the water.

Five Lamonts, now that is a slice of Chaos Theory. He lets me get in first, since I'm still blanking with the fly rod (on the Ribble that is). His early spring Ribble salmon continues to be the gift that keeps giving, and I wish I had a clicker for every time it rears its head. No conversation is safe, no matter how obscure, as he will invariably find a way to guide it towards that spring salmon.

Politics = spring salmon.

Music review = spring salmon.

Sporting triumph = spring salmon.

Moon landing = spring salmon.

Health scare = spring salmon.

Relationship problems = spring salmon.

International peace treaty = spring salmon.

Advancements in human evolution through science = spring salmon.

'*And*, do you know it was on the fly?'

On the fly! The fucking lunatic. No, 'the Captain' never thinks to mention his cowering in the weeds in a purple tracksuit, his Kojak negotiating skills or how he believes that a woodland sprite named Terry bestows luck upon him. He certainly isn't as bushy in telling folk about his recent whitey, either.

I'm more than happy to watch and listen to Lamont crow, though. That's what friends are for, after all. Mutual gratification is what fires me the most, and as I start to fish this wild run on the Ribble in early October, I can't help but feel a satisfying sense of contentment. I'm glad that I took the plunge and left the cracker factory to become my own boss. For the moment at least, it appears to be working, and rather than feeling trapped, I'm finding creativity around every corner. It can be hard to think when your nose is being pressed to the grindstone by middle management, and I'm grateful to the Ribble for making me brave; for introducing me to the occasional like-minded soul, who is also hooked on hope (I think psychologists call it confirmation bias); for bumping into people like Ahab, who have lived a life and a half, and are able to pass on their wisdom to the next generation. He once told me, 'Don't ever love in vain,' or at least that's what I think he said. It was either that or, 'Don't ever *live* in vain.' It was a very windy day, so it could have even been, 'Don't ever live in a van.' They're all sound pieces of advice, to be fair.

In the Ribble on this dull, cloudy, gusty autumn day, I am like a champion of life as I admire the natural woodland on the far bank, taking in the oranges, reds and yellows that portend the winter shutdown. According to the internet, orange is the colour of adventure and social communication, and it also radiates warmth, happiness, physical energy and stimulation. Who am I to argue with Google?

Speaking of the world's preeminent search engine, Lamont is one hundred percent certain that he thought of Google before Google did. I'm sceptical, though, as he also once claimed that it was his ancestors who invented the chair.

I start to single spey cast across the river. I've had a couple of fish from the tail of this run, so I'm fairly confident in my thirteen-foot vision catapult and full floater with a five-foot sink tip, connected by a fifteen-pound, six-foot cast to a barbless, double-hooked Verminator. Ideally, I'd have an eleven-foot switch rod for this beat, as it's overgrown and has overhanging trees on both banks, but I haven't got around to buying one yet, and I'm quietly hoping that they'll prove to be a flash in the pan (they won't). Wading through the pool isn't an easy task; it's heaving with submerged boulders, and there's a real knack to guiding yourself through and around them without tripping. Stealth is the order of the day in the top section, but with a foot of water on the river, it's easier said than done. I fish through this top forty metres without incident, while Lamont has decided to fish below our small club hut and has agreed to meet me there at lunchtime.

As I emerge from under the trees, the river straightens out into an attractive fly run, and on my third cast down, the line goes tight and I gently lift into a fish. My iPod is playing Get Duffy by Primal Scream, which is enhancing the experience no end. The fish goes on a long run, but I stand my ground and get it under control. It's a brightly-coloured cock fish of roughly seven pounds, and is quickly landed, unhooked, photographed and returned without fuss. These days, photographic evidence a requirement with any catch, so much so that

I've met anglers who say that they can't go out unless their phone is fully charged; imagine that! I'll always take a picture if it's convenient and appropriate, but you don't want to suffer death by social media, and the zero foreplay, blunt line of questioning from an online stranger, 'Where did you catch it, mate?'

What, not even a drink first?

I carry on down the beat, fishing all the way to the hut without any further excitement. Lamont is already there enjoying a coffee, and I show him the picture of the salmon. He immediately declares it a kipper (a fish that's ready to spawn), and I agree with the assessment as I pour myself a drink, sit down and unpack my lunch. Just as I'm about to take a first sip of warming coffee, my phone rings; it's an unrecognised number. Then, I sit in silence for five or six minutes, absorbing the contents of the call.

Ahab was found leaning on the huge trunk of an old conker tree yesterday, at a beat below Ribchester, dressed in his waders, boots and jacket, with his bag alongside him and his rod balanced across his legs. I was told that he slipped away after his heart gave up on him, while he was sat facing the same river that he had fished for nearly sixty-five years. Around his neck, hanging by a cord, were his reading glasses, and on his lap was an open tin filled with salmon flies. When the ambulance crew arrived, they found him looking totally at peace.

Lamont and I sit in silence for a moment. The news comes as a massive shock, but not really a surprise, as

Ahab's health had been on the slide for some time. I know that there was nothing wrong with his heart, though; it belonged to the River Ribble. Lamont suggests packing up and heading for the pub, but that's not what Ahab would have done.

'Let's fish the bottom beat,' I say, 'and *then* go the pub.'

We half-heartedly go through the motions for an hour or so, but we can't continue any longer than that. Ahab had once told me, 'Lad (I was in my forties at the time), there are three phases of salmon fishing. Phase one is wanting to get hold of every salmon in the river, but that eventually passes, and then all you want to do is catch the biggest. When you've finally got all that bullshit out of your system, you will be content just being out on the river. The reward is the journey, not the destination.'

I think that he got the most and the biggest well and truly out of his system many years ago, having caught hundreds of salmon from the Ribble, including a fish which bottomed a robust set of scales that only went up to thirty pounds (he'd described it as being so large, 'you could hear it swimming!'). He is gone, but we know that in many ways, it is only the beginning of his legend.

Sitting in the pub, we fire up the jukebox and listen to his favourite band, the Beatles (In My Life has us in tears), while we swap our favourite Ahab stories and lament the void that he leaves behind. We also sadly agree that as far as ways to bow out go, he nailed it perfectly.

Lamont compares it to the ultimate mic-drop moment, gently fading away there in his own church; talk about luck. He had fished every inch from Settle to Preston, and even though he knew that he had seen the best of the Ribble, he always remained optimistic for future generations. He was a rare angler in that respect. I think it was because he properly knew the Ribble system; he had lived for it.

Lamont and I make a pact not to fish for the remaining two weeks of the season. Ahab's death has knocked the stuffing out of us, but we will, as ever, go out for a muted beer on the last day of the season for the Salmon! Salmon! Salmon! (our WhatsApp group name) annual awards. Lamont is the frontrunner in the Salmon Weasel Award (a stuffed, mounted weasel), which is given for catching a salmon when you should be at work. His fine March salmon puts him firmly in the driving seat this year. Since I became fiendishly self-employed, I am omitted from the Weasel, but I've created another trophy to compete for, the Most Bastard. This impressive handmade, stoneware salmon sculpture is given for the digital bullet that makes a receiver verbally exhale the word, *Bastard!* I hope that my July salmon of twenty-plus will mop up, but you never know how the judging panel will lean. It's a tough, mean school, with forty salmon being landed (all returned) between fourteen of us. One of our number has had one over twenty pounds from the Hodder on a trout set-up, while another lucky sod had a fine nineteen-pound salmon on the fly, but the clear front runner for the Most

Bastard is Paul, who landed three salmon on the fly in a single afternoon session. Like with many awards, ours isn't above fickle opinions or even outright corruption. Half the fun is attempting to nobble the judges.

Today's date is 30 October 2019, and bright sunshine has temporarily chased the grey clouds away, giving us another classic, clear, beautiful autumn day. Lamont and I are sat on a bench with a brass plaque on it that reads, *RING IN SICK* (we put it there). This is the place where we first properly encountered Ahab, having walked him back through the wood after he'd got himself stuck in the mud, and where he had passed Lamont's 'Sooty or Sweep?' test with flying colours.

I have brought with me a two-year-old conker tree, which we are planting seven feet behind our bench. Every year, I plant conkers in pots and watch them grow with the kids, and we then decide where to do a spot of guerrilla gardening along the catchment. We dig a hole and securely plant the tree, and Lamont then offers up a Peng-like statement of 'A life for a life,' as we each take a slug of single malt. We turn and sit side by side on the bench; this is our spot. Unexpectedly, Lamont pulls out a small wireless Bluetooth speaker and plays Neil Young's classic track, Old Man.

I take a long look down the river that I love, and that has given me so much profound inner joy. We live in circles, we live in cycles, and as one completes, another begins.

'Who knows,' I break the silence, 'maybe in twenty years, I'll be an Ahab.'

Lamont leans into me and smiles, before taking a hit from his hip flask and, through laughing lips, he caustically hisses, 'You? ... You've no fucking chance.'

With Lamont's uplifting words still buzzing in my ears, it's time to put a lid on my 2019 season and slope off into the winter sunset to reflect, regenerate and prepare myself for next year's journey down the rabbit hole. Winter is for slow motion; it's time to tune into nature's rhythm, meaning less activity and more rest, and analogue as opposed to digital. If you're not tuned in, you're tuned out.

I'm typing this while sat next to my open fire. I have just poured myself a large glass of red wine and lowered the needle onto Jefferson Airplane's LP Surrealistic Pillow, and I am now immensely enjoying a sonic tidal wave of a track, White Rabbit.

Remember what the dormouse said.

The End